THE

Family Music Book

PRINTED IN THE U.S.A.

THE
Family Music Book

A COLLECTION OF OVER THREE HUNDRED PIECES OF PIANO, ORGAN AND VOCAL MUSIC OF MODERATE DIFFICULTY, SELECTED FROM THE WORKS OF CLASSIC AND MODERN COMPOSERS AND INCLUDING MANY OLD FAVORITES

GROSSET & DUNLAP · NEW YORK

Published by

G. SCHIRMER, INC., NEW YORK

Contents

PIANO

Piano Favorites

Selections from Operas

Easy Classics

Marches

Waltzes

Dances

Jigs, Reels, Country Dances

Piano Duets

Sunday Music

ORGAN

Hammond Chord Organ

Hammond Spinet Organ

VOCAL

Favorite Ballads and Songs

Stephen Foster

Negro Spirituals

Gilbert and Sullivan

Children's Songs

Children's Songs (Continued)

Sacred Songs

Hymns

Christmas

National Songs

Patriotic Songs

In the Gipsy Camp

Edited and fingered by
Louis Oesterle

Franz Behr, Op. 424, No. 3

Allegretto con moto

marcato
Ped.

a tempo
riten. un poco
pp
mf
f
Ped.

p
grazioso
mf
p
f
un poco più lento
p
riten. un poco
a tempo
pp

mf
f
ff
ffz
Ped.

Little Sweetheart

Enfant chéri

Revised and fingered by
Wm Scharfenberg

C. BOHM

Moderato

f
p
Ped.
staccato.
cresc.
f
Ped.
p
cresc.
f
ff

p
ff
Ped.
p
cresc.
p

cresc.
ff
f
p
mf
f
mf
Ped.

Ped.
cresc.
Ped.
f
p
staccato
cresc.
f
p
Ped.

cresc.
stringendo.

Scarf-Dance

Der Schärpentanz

Scène de Ballet

Revised and fingered by
Wm Scharfenberg

C. CHAMINADE

delicatamente
dim.
cresc.
pp rubato
dim.
cresc.
dim.
Ped.

p delicatamente
dim.
pp
cresc.
f
dim.
p
pp rubato.
cresc.
f
dim.
p
pp
rit.
f secco

Valse

Edited by Carl Deis

Auguste Durand, Op. 33

f
Ped.
cresc.
p
ff
1.
2.

mf ritmato
f
1.
2.
p e leggero
cre - - - - scen -
do
f di - - - mi - nu - - en - do
p
cre - - - - scen - - - do
Ped.
*

f
di - mi - nu - en - do
p
mf ritmato
f
ff
rit.
a tempo
p
cresc.
ff
ff
Ped.

f
Ped.
p
cresc.
ff

pp
poco cresc
mf
brillante
cresc.
f
mf
cresc.
poco a
poco
f
brillante
cresc.
ff
f
ff

Humoreske

Edited and fingered by
Louis Oesterle

Anton Dvořák. Op. 101, №7

Poco lento e grazioso (♩= 72)

Ped.
a tempo
rit. fz dim.
pp
cresc.
rit.

Original * 

pp
Ped.
rit.
a tempo
f
dim.
p
dim.
rit.
p dim.
pp

Salut d'amour
Love's Greeting

Edited and fingered by
Louis Oesterle

Edward Elgar. Op. 12

cresc.
a tempo
pp
ppp
p dolce
rit.
f
mf
cresc. molto
sf dim.
dim.
rit. pp
Ped.

pp
a tempo
poco string.
Ped.
Tempo I
rit.
pp
cresc.
p
cresc.
dim.
pp
cresc.

accel.
ff
f
ff
p
stacc.
Ped.
cresc. molto
ff rit.
largamente
sf
p rit.
pp l.h.
Tempo più lento
più lento
pp
ppp
rit.
a tempo
pp rall. e dim.

La Cinquantaine

Air dans le style ancien

Revised and fingered by
Wm Scharfenberg

GABRIEL MARIE

Andantino ($\text{𝅗𝅥} = 88$)

mf
Ped.
p
cresc.
f
sf
tr
sotto voce
pp

cresc.
f
Ped.
Ped.
sotto voce
f
pp
cresc.
Ped.
Ped.
f
decresc.
pp
cresc.
f rit.
a tempo
f
Ped.
Ped.

decresc.
pp
cresc.
f
rit.
p
Ped.
Ped.
a tempo
sf
tr
p

sf
Ped.
mf
p
cresc.
f
allargando
sf

Echoes of the Ball

Intermezzo

Revised and fingered by
Wm Scharfenberg

ERNEST GILLET

Tempo di Valse

a tempo
rit.
ppp
pppp
ppp
ppp
cresc. ed animato poco a poco.
sf
pp
ppp
ff

ppp
mf
ppp
dim.
pp
cresc.
mp
cresc.
cresc. ed animato poco a poco

un poco dim. e rit.
pp
a tempo
mf
f
Tempo I
ppp
ppp
cresc.
ed animato poco a poco
sf pp
ppp
Presto
dim.

Berceuse
from "Jocelyn"

Edited and fingered by
LOUIS OESTERLE

B. Godard

Andantino (♩= 108)
p
cresc.
p
pp
pp
rall.
Recit.
"Ca - chés dans cet a - sile où Dieu nous a con - duits."
"Con - cealed in this re - treat where - to we have been led."
mf
parlando
pp
cresc.
mf

cresc.
Ped.
Andante. (♩= 69)
Oh! ne t'é - veil - le pas en - cor.
"Oh! wake not yet from out thy dream!"
pp
l.h.
p
cantabile ed espressivo.
cresc.
il canto marcato.
r.h.
tranquillo.
mf

Andantino.
l.h.
r.h.
l.h.
p
cresc
Ped.
p
pp
Récit.
rall.
mf
parlando.
pp
cresc.
mf
cresc.
pp
l.h.

Andante.
cantabile ed espressivo.
molto cresc.
dim.
il canto marcato.
r.h.
tranquillo.
molto ritenuto.

Album-Leaf
Albumblatt

Revised and fingered by W.S.

Edvard Grieg
Op.12, No 7.

Carnival of Venice

Italian popular melody
of the early 19th century
Arranged by Luis Jordá

Meno mosso
Ped.
Poco lento
p
Allegretto
mf

Con moto
Vivo

Idilio

Edited and fingered by
LOUIS OESTERLE

Théodore Lack. Op. 134

poco rit.
mf
cresc.
f
dim.
Ped.
pp

poco
a poco cresc.
f
dim. e rall.
p
mf
p
mf
p rit.
pp delicatamente
8
pp
l. h.
rall.

Flower Song

Blumenlied

Revised and fingered by
Wm Scharfenberg

Gustav Lange

Lento

cresc.
f
rit.
pp
rapido
zeffiroso
rit. poco
31
mf espressivo
Ped.

mf con anima cantando
cresc.
rit. molto
f
a piacere rit. cresc. riten.
a tempo
mf
Ped.

rit. dimin.
mf
espressivo
p
dimin. a
poco a poco
cresc.
lento molto
f
p tranquillo
Ped.

Liebestraum No. 3

Franz Liszt
Arranged by Juan Jaume

mf
cresc.
sempre cresc.
f
dim.
Più animato
mf

più f
f
a piacere
Tempo I°
p
una corda

Ped.
dim.
sf
p
pp

To a Wild Rose

from "Woodland Sketches"

Edward MacDowell, Op. 51 No. 1

With simple tenderness ♩= 88

ritard.
p
p
mp
slightly marked
p
pp
ppp

Élegie

Mélodie

from incidental music to Leconte de Lisle's drama "Les Érinnyes"

Jules Massenet, Op. 10, No.5
Arranged by Carl Deis

a tempo
f
dim. e rit.
p
f
espress.
p
ff
mf
molto dim.
Ped.
a tempo
pp
allargando
p
pp

Serenata

Revised and fingered by
Wm Scharfenberg

M. MOSZKOWSKI. Op. 15, No 1

rinfz.
mp
cresc.
sfz
f
dimin.
molto ritard.
pp
Ped.

a tempo
Ped.
riten.
marc.
un poco
pp

Narcissus

ETHELBERT NEVIN. Op.13, No. 4.

Andante con moto.

Published by The Boston Music Co.
Used by Permission

tranquillo
3
p cresc.
il basso una corda
f

mf
vivo
dim. senza rit.
scherzando
ff
sf
sf
Tempo I.
p

m. g.
3
p
m. g.
1-3
rit.
p

Menuet

Edited and fingered by
L. Vollmer

I. J. Paderewski. Op. 14. № 1

Allegretto

f
ff
Ped.
8
rapidamente
a tempo
1.
2.

con forza la melodia
Ped.
p
sf
mf
cre - - scen - - do
f
rallent.

a tempo
pp
Ped.
cresc.
f
ff
rapidamente
a tempo

Coda.
Vivo.
p
accel.
f
mf
l. h.
Ped.

Poupée Valsante

Edited and fingered by
Louis Oesterle

Ed. Poldini

pp

Ped.
f
dim.
p
pp
8

p
pp
Ped.
1.
2.

p
cantabile
Ped.
dimin.
p
8
f

dimin.
p
Ped.
pp
ppp
smorzando
8
Ped.

Edited and fingered by
Louis Oesterle

Prélude

(Andante)

S. RACHMANINOFF. Op.3, No. 2

Agitato
mf
cresc.
dim.
mf
cresc.
dim.
cresc.

ff
dim.
cresc.
fff

sfff
ff
Tempo I
fff pesante
sffff
Ped.

sffff
sffff
dim.
dim.
dim.
mf
ppp
dim.
mf
ppp
Ped.

Mélodie in F

Revised by Carl Deis

Anton Rubinstein, Op. 3, No. 1

p
p
mf
f
cresc.
p stringendo
rit.

a tempo
p
p
p
mf
f
cresc.
p stringendo
rit.
Come
p

primo
cresc.
p
p
mp quasi cadenza
poco deliberato
più corrente
poco rit.
p
pp
Ped.

The Swan

From "The Carnival of Animals"

Camille Saint-Saëns
Arranged by Henry Levine

Andante (♩ - 72)

mp
p
poco rit.

a tempo
p
mf
dim.
p
pp
rit.

Rustles of Spring

Frühlingsrauschen

Edited and fingered by
Louis Oesterle

CHRISTIAN SINDING
Op. 32, Nº 3

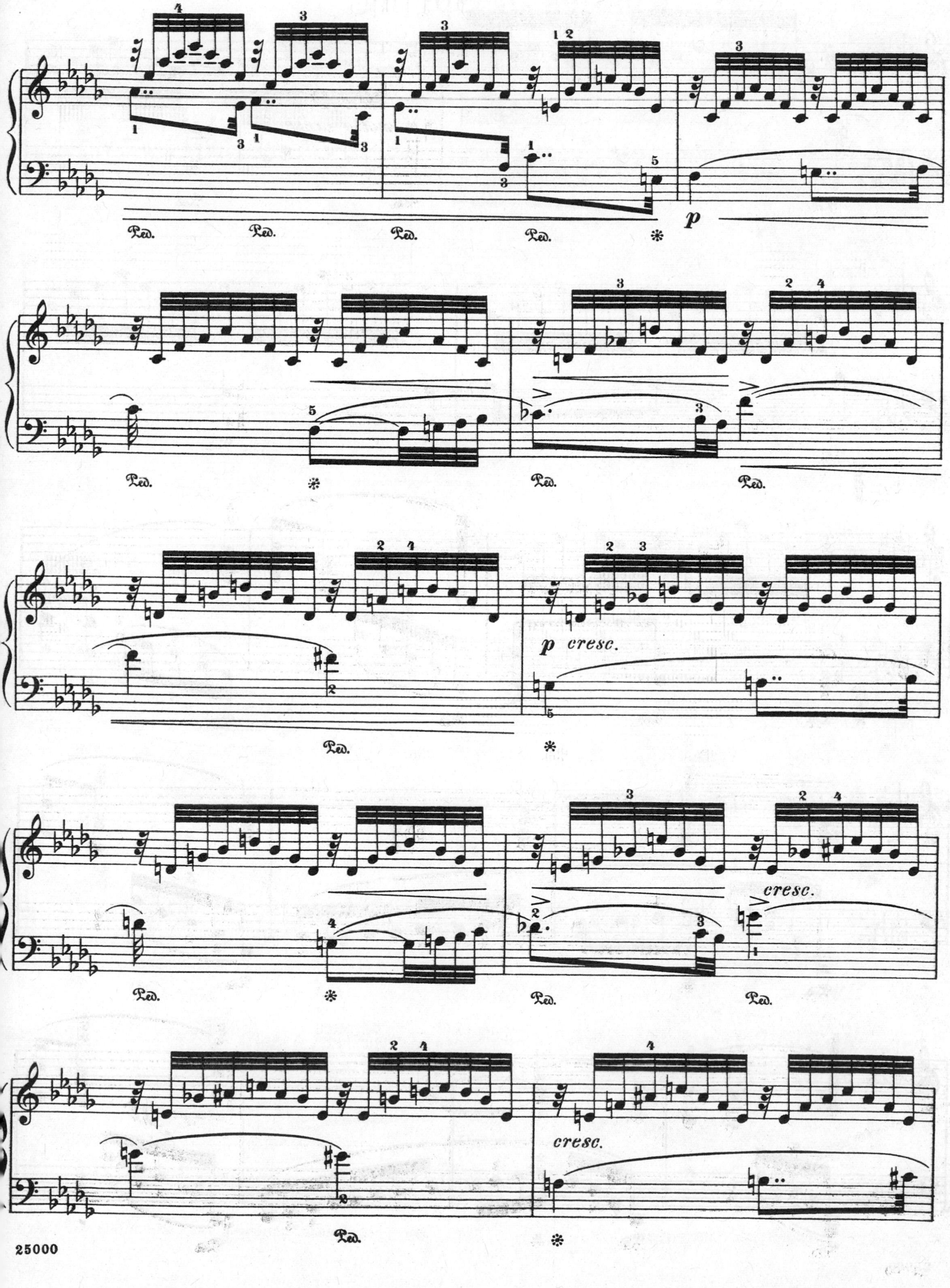
Ped.
p
p cresc.
cresc.

molto cresc.
ff
r. h.
sempre ff

fz
Ped.

ff
dim.
pp
Ped.

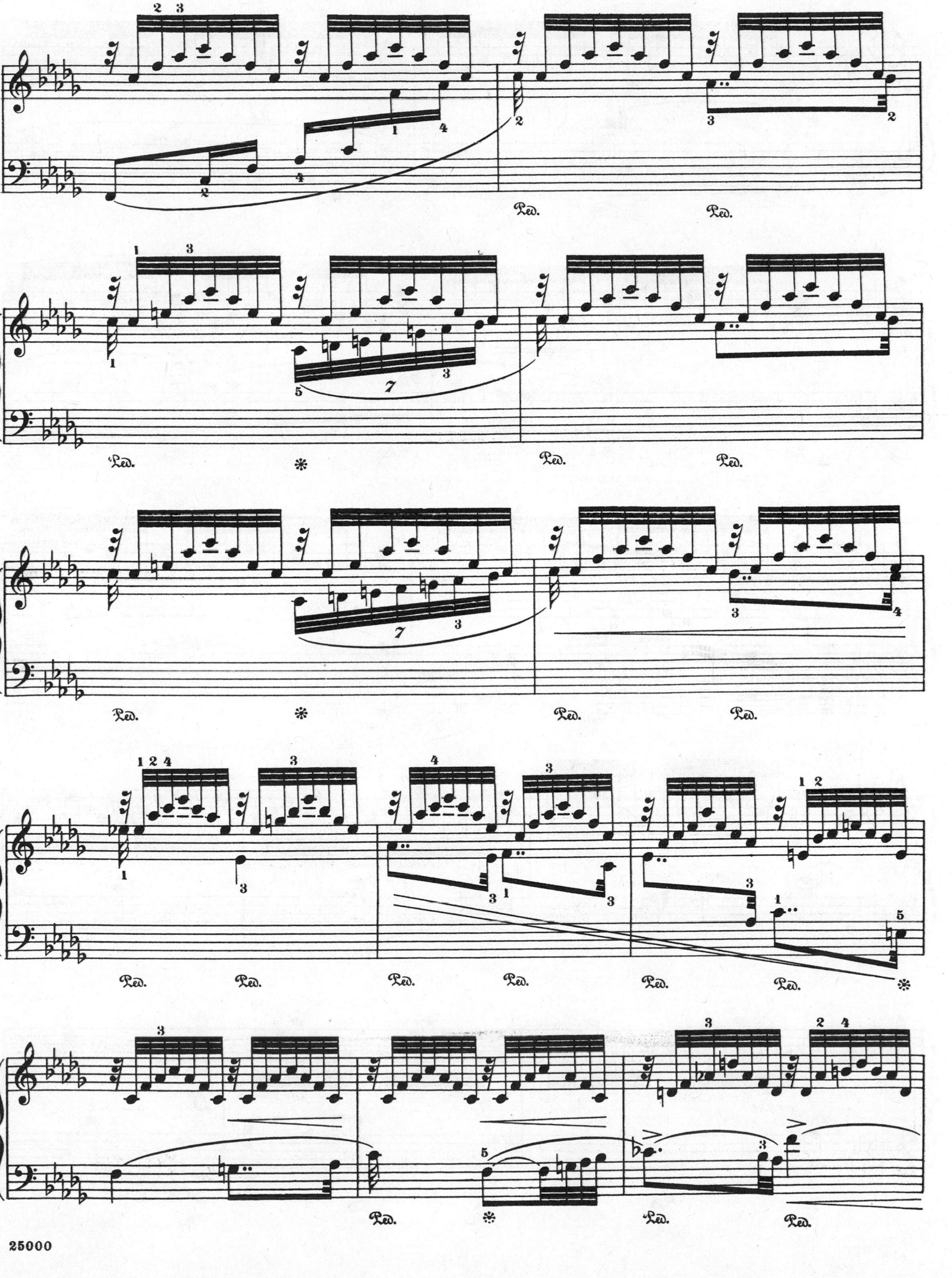

cresc.
cresc.
ff

Ped.
ff

Chant sans paroles

Song without words

Revised and fingered by
Wm Scharfenberg

P. TSCHAIKOWSKY

Allegretto grazioso e cantabile

f
m.g.
Tempo I
poco rit.
m.g.
dim.
p
marcato
f
energico
cresc.

ff
dim.
p
f
cresc.
ff
dim.
p
p
sempre di-mi-nu-en-do
marcato la melodia
pp
ppp

Hearts and Flowers
(Coeurs et Fleurs)

Theo. M. Tobani

Published, 1950, by The Boston Music Co.
Used by Permission

mf
f
ff
p
dim.
mf
p espressivo
mf
p
p

mf
p
mf
mf
ff
tr
p
mf
p
mf
mf
p
pp

March from "Aïda"

GIUSEPPE VERDI

Allegro maestoso

ff
f
molto cresc.
ff

Musetta's Waltz-Song

from "La Bohème"

Giacomo Puccini

poco allarg.
a tempo
ritenendo molto
p
a tempo
molto rall.
rit.
a tempo
8
pp
8
molto rit.

a tempo
mf
pp rall.
morendo
a tempo
pp
quasi rit.
poco rit.
poco allarg.
a tempo

Toreador Song

from "Carmen"

Georges Bizet
Arranged by D. Savino

r.h.
l.h.
a tempo, poco meno
f poco rit.
l.h.

f
p
cresc.
f
molto dim.
pp
poco rit.

a tempo
ff
pp
poco rit.
a tempo
ff
ff

Cavalleria rusticana

Intermezzo sinfonico

P. Mascagni,
arr. by Max Spicker

Andante sostenuto

Ped.
con forza
p
dim.
pp

Menuetto

From "Don Giovanni"

W. A. Mozart

f
p

March
from "Faust"

Charles Gounod
Arranged by D. Krug

Tempo di marcia

ff
March
con spirito
ff

p
cresc.
p

cresc.
f
cresc.
con spirito
ff
p

mf
f
ff
Ped.
Ped.
ff
fffz

Bridal Song
from "Lohengrin"

Revised and fingered by
Wm Scharfenberg

R. Wagner

dim.
p
p
Ped.
mf
R. H.
cresc.
f
p dolce

Vesti la giubba
from "Pagliacci"

English version by
Henry Grafton Chapman

R. Leoncavallo

p
Canio
Re - ci - tar! Men - tre pre - so dal de - li -
To go on! When my head's whirl - ing with mad -
rio non so più quel che di - co e quel che fac - cio! Ep - pur è
ness, not know - ing what I'm say - ing or what I'm do - ing! Yet I have

string un poco
d'uo - po... sfor - za - ti! Bah! sei tu forse un uom?
got to force my - self! Pshaw! can't you be a man?
col canto
precipitato
(laughing bitterly)
Ah! ah! ah! ah! ah!
Ha! ha! ha! ha! ha!
rit.
(taking his head in his hands in despair)
Tu se' Pa - gliac - cio!
You're a Pa - gliac - cio!
pp
Adagio (♩= 46)
declamando con dolore
Ve - sti la giub - ba e la fac - cia in - fa - ri - na.
Put on your smock, now, smear your face with the pow - der!
La gen - te pa - ga e ri - der vuo - le qua.
The peo - ple pay you, and they must have their fun!
portando

E se Ar-lec - chin t'in - vo-la Co - lum - bi - na, ri - di, Pa -
If Har - le - quin your Col - um - bine take from you, Laugh loud, Pa -
violento
Opp.
gliac - cio e o - gnun ap - plau - di - rà! Tra - mu - ta in
gliac - cio, and all will shout, "Well done!" Change in - to
poco rit.
a tempo
affrett.
laz - zi lo spa - smo ed il pian - to; in u - na
laugh - ter your sigh - ing and weep - ing, Aye, let gri -
col canto
a tempo
col canto
cresc. rit.
smor - fia il sin - ghioz - zo e'l do - lor... Ah!
mac - es of sob - bing play the part! Ah!
cresc. poco rit.

a piena voce, straziante
Ri- di, Pa - gliac - cio, sul tuo a - mo - re in -
Laugh, O Pa - gliac - cio, for your love that is
f
con grande espressione
fran - to! Ri - di del duol che t'av - ve -
ru - in'd! Laugh to the pain that now is
cedendo
(sobbing)
Lo stesso movimento
le - na il cor!
gnaw - ing your heart!
cantabile con molta espressione
mf
sonoro
r.h.
marcato il canto
r.h.

La donna è mobile
Woman so changeable
Canzone from the Opera
"RIGOLETTO"

English version by
Sigmund Spaeth

Giuseppe Verdi

Allegretto
p
marcato
con brio
La don-na è mo-bi-le qual piu-ma al
Wo-man so change-a-ble, Swayed like a
pp
legato
ven-to, mu-ta d'ac-cen-to e di pen-sie-ro. Sem-pre un a-
feath-er! None can tell wheth-er He should be-lieve her. Seem-ing so

pp
ma-bi-le, leg-gia-dro vi-so, in pian-to o in ri-so, è men-zo-
am-ia-ble, Al-ways be-guil-ing, Tear-ful or smil-ing, Still a de-
pp
gne-ro. La donna è mo-bil qual piu-ma al ven-to, mu-ta d'ac-
ceiv-er! Wo-man ca-pri-cious, Swayed like a feath-er! None can tell
p
f
leggiero
cen-to e di pen-sier, e di pen-
wheth-er He should be-lieve! Should he be-
f
pp
p
sier, e,
lieve? Ah!
pp
f

con forza
e___ di pen - sier.
Should he be - lieve?
ff
p marcato
p
È sem - pre mi - se - ro chi a lei s'af -
Lo, how great mis - er - y With him a -
pp
fi - da, chi le con - fi - da, mal - cau - to il co - re! Pur mai non
bid - eth, Who - so con - fid - eth In all her grac - es! But true fe -
sen - te - si fe - li - ce ap - pie - no chi su quel se - no
li - ci - ty By him is wast - ed Who ne'er hath tast - ed
pp

non li-ba a - mo - re! La__ don-na è mo - bil qual__ piu-ma al
Love's fond em - brac - es! Light-heart-ed wo - man, Swayed like a
p
leggiero
f
pp
ven - to, mu - ta d'ac - cen - to e__ di pen - sier,
feath - er! None can tell wheth - er He__should be - lieve.
pp
e__ di pen - sier, e,
Should he be - lieve? Ah!
p
p
con forza
e__ di__ pen - sier!
Should he__ be - lieve?
f
ff

Quartet
from "Rigoletto"

Giuseppe Verdi
Arranged by D. Savino

r.h.
mf
l.h.
f
stent.
3
r.h.
p
l.h.
r.h.
p
l.h.
r.h.
l.h.
f
poco rit.

a tempo
p
pp
pp
cresc.
rit. assai
ff
f
a tempo
p
pp
pp

cresc.
rit. assai
ff
f
pp
f rit.
a tempo
pp
f rit.
(Più lento)
p
pp
p
pp
morendo
p
pp

Song of India

From the legend "Sadko"

Transcribed by Carl Deis

N. Rimsky-Korsakow

p

f
r.h.
l.h.
mf
Ped.

r.h.
l.h.
meno f
Ped.
mp
p
poco ritenuto
8
pp
rall.

149

Barcarolle

Intermezzo from the opera "Les Contes d'Hoffmann"

Moderato

J. Offenbach

sempre più dolce
morendo
ppp

Pilgrims' Chorus and Sextet

From the opera "Tannhäuser"

Richard Wagner
Arranged by D. Savino

Lento
fp
tr
p
cresc.
8
poco allarg.
f

To the Evening Star

O du mein holder Abendstern

from "Tannhäuser"

English version by
Dr. Th. Baker

Richard Wagner

Moderato (𝅗𝅥 = 46)
dolce
Wie To - des - ah - nung, Dämm'-rung deckt die
Fo - rier di mor - te, già il cre - pu - scol
Fore - bod - ing death - gloom, dusk the vale has
p
Ped. * Ped. * Ped. * Ped. *
Lan - de, umhüllt das Thal mit schwärz - li - chem Ge - wan - de;
ca - de, di ne - ro ve - lo av - vol - ta è già la val - le!
cloud - ed, Her mist - y wind - ing - sheet has all en - shroud - ed;
p
Ped. * Ped. * Ped. * Ped. *
der See - le, die nach je - nen Höh'n ver - langt, vor ih - rem
e l'al - ma, che già a - spi - ra ver - so il ciel; pria di par -
The soul, — in - tent on yon un - fad - ing height, In fear would
Ped. * Ped. * Ped. * Ped. * Ped. *

Flug durch Nacht und Grau - sen bangt. Da scheinest
tir pre-sa è d'or - ren - do gel! La splen-di
fain a-void that aw - ful flight. Then shin-est
p p p pp
Ped. * Ped. *
du, o lieb-lich-ster der Ster-ne! dein sanf-tes Licht ent-
tu, bel - l'a-stro in-can - ta - to - re, e su noi span - di il
thou, O star, of all the fair-est! With us be - low thy
pp
sen-dest du der Fer-ne, die nächt'-ge Dämm'rung theilt dein lie-ber
dol - ce tuo chia - ro - re; tu squar-ci il ve - lo ch'avvol - ge l'e - mi -
mel-low light thou shar-est; Dim shades of night-fall yield be-fore thy
pp
Strahl, und freund - lich zeigst du den Weg aus dem Thal.
sfer, e del - la val - le a noi mo-stri il sen - tier!
ray, Whose friend - ly beam thro' the vale shows our way.
p p

Andante mosso
p
più p
p dolce, espress.
pp
pp
O! du mein hol - der A - - bend-stern, wohl grüsst' ich
Oh! tu bel - l'a - stro in - can - - ta - tor, che span - di
O thou mine own fair star of eve, Wel - come to
im - - mer dich so gern; vom
pa - - ce al mon - - do in - ter, a
thee I ev - - er gave; Greet
p
p
pp
Her - zen, das sie nie ver - rieth, grü - sse sie.
te ri - vol - ge il me - - sto cor, d'a - mo - re
thou my faith - ful heart's dear love When soon she

wenn sie vor - bei dir zieht, wenn sie ent - schwebt dem
l'ul - ti - mo gen - til pen - sier, co - lei fra po - co a
near - eth thy home a - bove; When, far from Earth and
Thal der Er - den, ein sel' - ger En - gel
te d'ac - can - to s'en vo - le - rà qual
all it bear - eth, To live an an - gel
dort zu wer - den, wenn sie ent -
an - - giol san - to, co - - - lei fra
yon she far - eth; When, far from
schwebt dem Thal der Er - den, ein
po - co a te d'ac - - can - to s'en
Earth and all it bear - eth, To
p
pp
poco rit.
più p
ppp

più rit.
cresc.
lento
dim.
pp
sel' - ger En - gel dort zu wer -
vo - le - rà qual an - giol san -
live an an - gel yon she far -
più rit.
poco cresc.
p
Ped.
a tempo
den.
to!
eth.
dolce, espress.
a tempo
p
p
p
più p
pp rit.
pp

Meditation from "Thaïs"

J. Massenet

Andante religioso
pp
col pedale
p
rall.
a tempo
sf
ppp subito
cresc.
f
dim.
p
cresc.
p rall.
dim.

a tempo
mf
più f
poco a poco appassionato
f
p calmato
Ped.
cresc.
f poco più appassionato
Piu mosso agitato
più f
sff
sf
p rall.

Tempo I°
pp
p
f rall.
Ped.
a tempo
Ped.
cresc.
f
p

cresc.
rall.
a tempo
sf
dim.
p
p
sf
dim.
calmato

La Traviata

(Duet: Alfred-Violetta)

Giuseppe Verdi
Arranged by D. Savino

p
cresc.
ff
dim.
1.
2.
poco rit.
poco rit.
Poco meno
pp
(a piacere)
(senza misura)
ppp
pp
f
pp
pp
allarg. dim.
l.h.

Arioso

Johann Sebastian Bach
Transcribed for Piano Solo by
Max Pirani

espress.
mf
Ped.
simile
cresc.
f
Ped.
Ped.
3
mp
pp
Ped.
simile
largamente
cresc.
3
cresc.
Ped.
Ped.
mp
poco rit.
Ped. Ped. Ped. Ped.

a tempo
sonore
p
pp
Ped.
simile
tr
cresc.
1.
allargando
a tempo
f
(mp)
2.
molto rit.

Minuet

Animato (♩ = 144) J. S. Bach

Albumblatt

"Für Elise"

Edited by Carl Deis

Ludwig van Beethoven

mf
dim.
a tempo
dim. e rit.
pp
dolce
cresc.
dim.
p
p

a tempo
dim. e poco rit.
pp
mf
dim.
p
dim. e rit.
a tempo
pp
p
cresc.
f
dim.
p
cresc.
f

dim.
p
pp
cresc.
dim.
a tempo
pp rall.
mf
dim.
p
dim.
pp
morendo
Ped.

Minuet
from
Sonata Op. 49, No. 2

Ludwig van Beethoven

Tempo di Menuetto (♩ = 112)

cresc.
f
p
p
poco rit.
pp

a tempo.
p
cresc.
mp
cresc.
f
f
p
p
p
cresc.
f dimin.

pp
p
cresc.
mp
cresc.
Coda.
f
p
p
mf
cresc.
f
poco rit.
pp

First Movement
of the
Sonata quasi una Fantasia
(Moonlight Sonata)

Adagio sostenuto (𝅗𝅥 = 52)

Ludwig van Beethoven
Op. 27, No. 2

a) It is evident that the highest part, as the melody, requires a firmer touch than the accompanying triplet-figure; and the first note in the latter must never produce the effect of a doubling of the melody in the lower octave.

b) A more frequent use of the pedal than is marked by the editor, and limited here to the most essential passages, is allowable; it is not advisable, however, to take the original directions *sempre senza sordini* (i. e., without dampers) too literally.

una corda.
pp
marcato, ma sempre p
cresc.
dimin.
p una corda.
pp
il basso sempre ten.
p
pp

a) The player must guard against carrying his hand back with over-anxious haste. For, in any event, a strict pedantic observance of time is out of place in this period, which has rather the character of an improvisation.

a) The notes with a dash above them may properly be dwelt upon in such a way as to give them the effect of suspensions, e. g., : in fact, a utilization of the inner parts, in accordance with the laws of euphony and the course of the modulation, is recommended throughout the piece.

Waltz

Edited by Carl Deis

Johannes Brahms. Op. 39, No. 15

f
dim.
p
(poco ritenuto - - - - - -)
p
(poco largamente - - - - - - -
poco cresc.
f
dim.
p dolce
(poco ritenuto - - - - -)

a Madame Camilla Pleyel

Nocturne

Edited and fingered by
Rafael Joseffy

F. CHOPIN. Op. 9, No. 2

Andante (♪ = 132)

cresc.
poco ritard.
a tempo
poco rall.
a tempo
fzp

p
pp
poco rubato
sempre pp
dolcissimo
p
con forza
stretto
ff senza tempo
cresc.
f
dim.
rallent. e smorz.
a tempo
pp
ppp

Two Preludes

Edited and fingered by
Carl Deis

F. Chopin. Op. 28, No. 7

Andantino (𝅗𝅥.= 72 senza rigore)

Largo (𝅗𝅥 = 44 giusto)

Op. 28, No. 20

A Madame Nathaniel de Rothschild

Valse

Revised and fingered by
Rafael Joseffy

F. Chopin. Op. 64, Nº 2

Tempo giusto

Più mosso
pp
Ped.
8

Più lento
mf
Ped.
dolce
poco ritenuto

Più mosso

Tempo I°
mf
*) Klindworth:

Più mosso
pp

Gipsy Rondo

(Hungarian Rondo)

Revised and fingered by
Wm Scharfenberg

Josef Haydn
Transcribed by L. Köhler

cresc.
f
fz
p
ff

Minore I

Maggiore

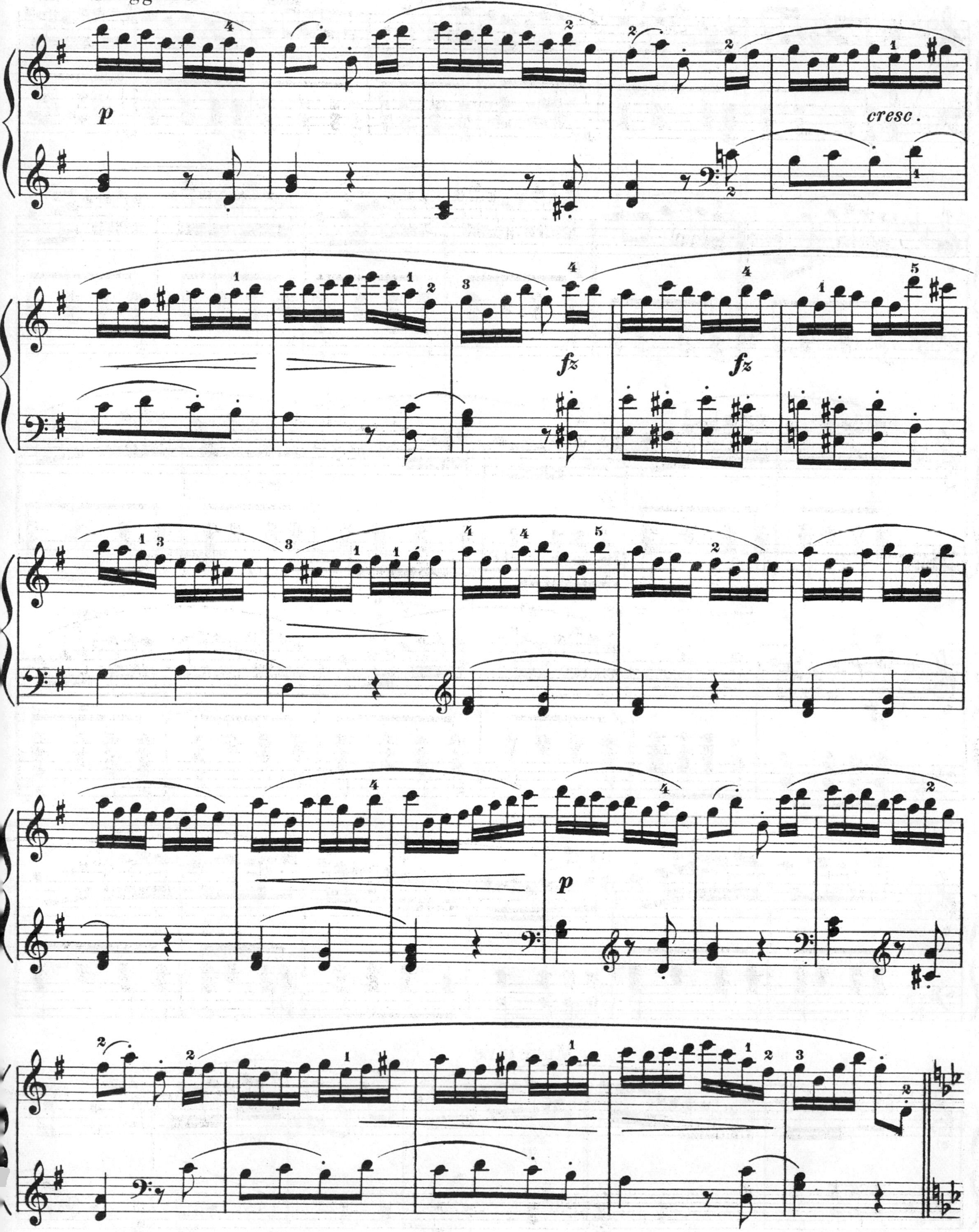
p
cresc.
fz
fz
p

Minore II
f
p
cresc.
p
p
f
Maggiore
p

cresc.
fz
fz
f
dim.
p
f
fz
p
cresc.
f
ff

Spring-Song

Allegretto grazioso (♩ = 88)

F. Mendelssohn

Composed in 1842.

a) The letters *o.* and *u.* indicate where the left hand is best placed over *(o.)* and under *(u.)* the right.

p
dimin.
grazioso
pp
Ped. come sopra
cresc.
al
f
sf
dim.

f
dimin.
p
cresc.
p dolce
cresc.
p dolce
grazioso
dimin.
pp
leggiero
Ped.ten.

Rondo Alla Turca

Allegretto (♩= 126)

W. A. MOZART

a)

b) Play the first A in the bass with the C sharp in the right hand.

f
p leggiero
cresc.
p
f pesante
Ped.
ten.

P.T.
T.P.
p
mp
Ped.
p
cresc.
f:p
tr
S.T.
T.S.
f
1.
2.
CODA

a) Play the four notes in either hand simultaneously.

b) 

Theme from

Sonata III

[K. 545]

Edited by
Richard Epstein
Abridged by C. D.

Wolfgang Amadeus Mozart

mp
tr
p
mp
p
mp
mf
p
cresc.
f
Ped.
tr
Ped.
Ped. Ped.

Impromptu

Allegretto (♩ = 132) F. SCHUBERT. Op. 142

Trio
pp
Ped. simile
decresc.
pp
f
cresc.
8
ff
sf
sf

sf
sf
sf
sf
sf
dim.
p
decresc.
Ped. simile
decresc.
pp
decresc.

pp sempre legato
f
ff
sff
p
sff
p
pp
pp
cresc.
ritard.
p

Moments Musicaux

(No. 3)

Edited and fingered by
G. BUONAMICI

F. Schubert. Op. 94

Allegro moderato (♩= 96)

*) May also be played thus:

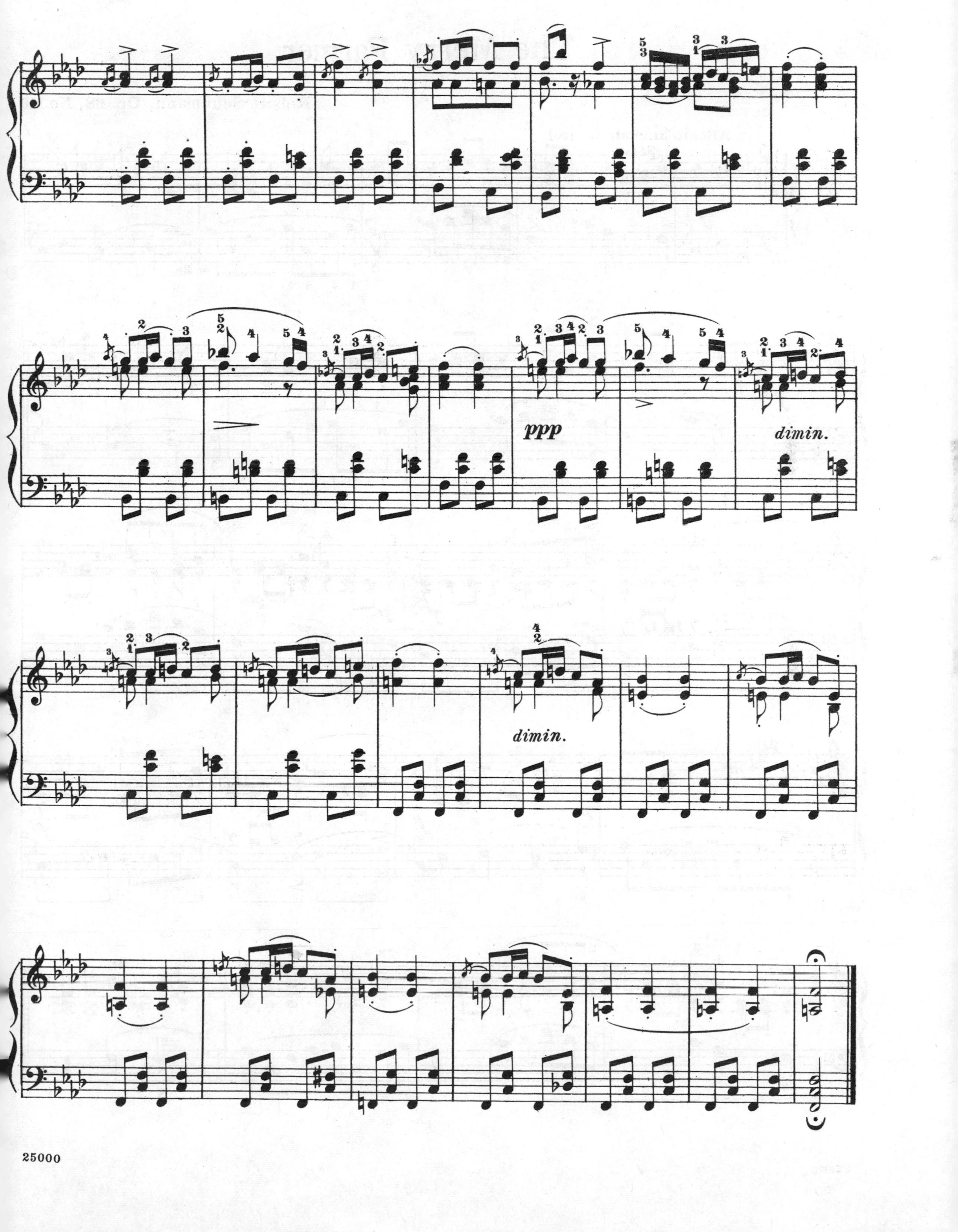
ppp
dimin.
dimin.

The Merry Farmer

Robert Schumann, Op. 68, No. 10

Allegro animato (𝅗𝅥 = 120)

Träumerei

R. SCHUMANN. Op. 15, № 7

Moderato (♩ = 100)

p
Ped.
ritard.
a tempo.
mf
cresc.
dim.
ritard.
a tempo
ri - tar - dan - do
p

25000

ROMANZE

Più moto (♩ = 130) Op. 68. № 19

p
fp
sfp
f
sf
Ped.
dim.
pp
sfz
dim. e ritard.

Tempo I.
pp sempre.
ritard.
a tempo.
cresc.
dim.
ritard.
piu p
sempre dim.
molto riten.
e smorz.
ppp

American Patrol

March

F. W. Meacham
Arranged by Chester Wallis

pp
p
poco a poco cresc.
Patrol gradually approaches
mf

marcato
mf poco a poco cresc.

*This upper part can be played an octave higher, if preferred, to *"loco"* which means in the written position.

* This may also be played an octave higher or first time in written position, second time an octave higher.

Drum call
f
mf

Patrol gradually retiring
dim.
p
p
poco a poco dim.
pp

Patrol disappears
ppp
f
mf
stringendo e cresc.
Vivo
ff
sff

El Capitan

March

John Philip Sousa

Marziale ♩. = 120

25000

p
p
cresc. molto

f grandioso
fff

Exhibition March

PHILIPP FAHRBACH, jr. Op. 263

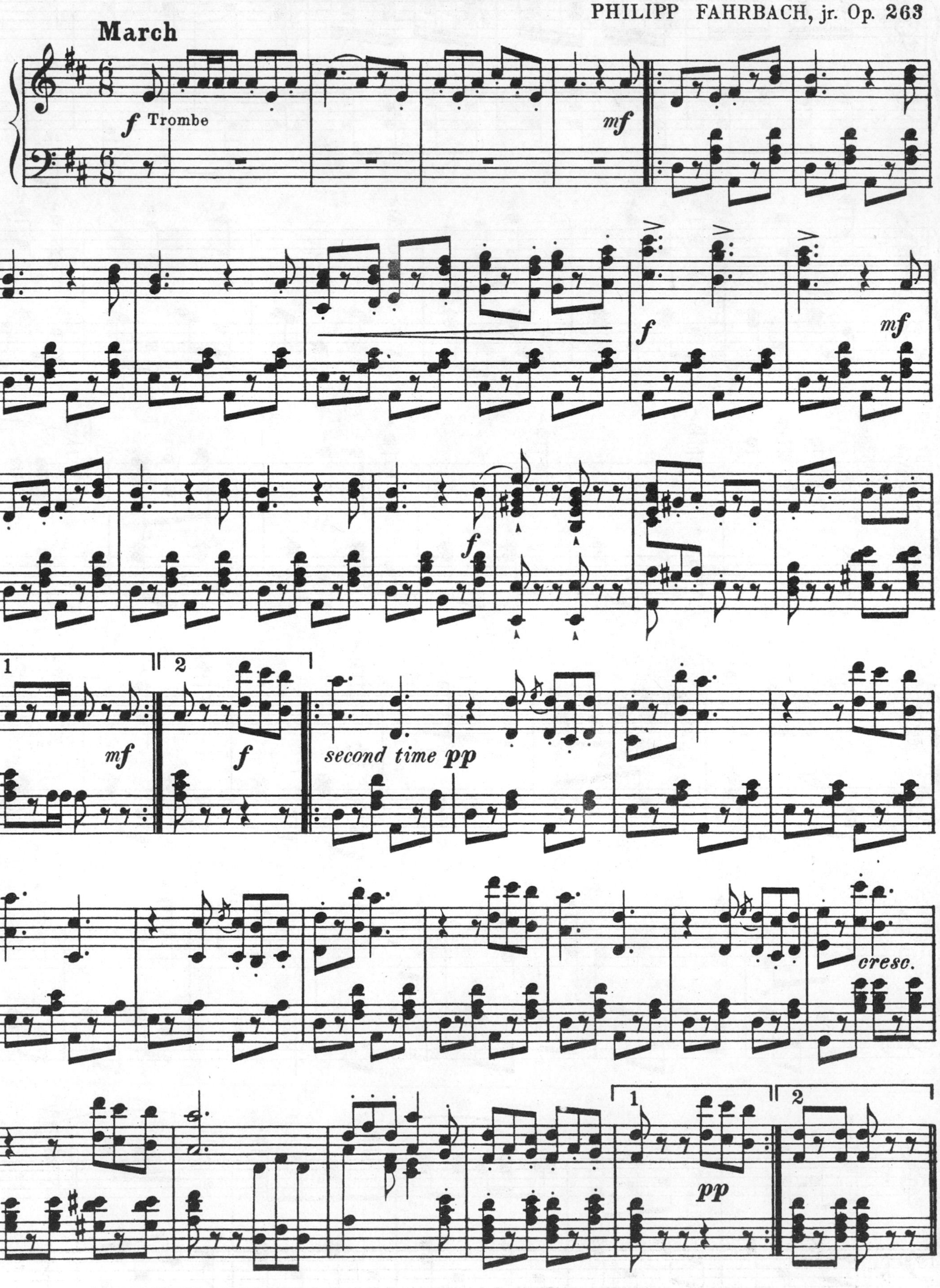

Trio.
f
p
mf
1
2

f Trombe
mf
f
mf
1
2
mf
f
second time pp
cresc.
1
2
pp
Fine.

Excerpt from "Cortége du Sardar"

(March of the Sardar)

Ippolitov-Ivanov
Arranged by Chester Wallis

Alla marcia maestoso

mf
cresc.
r. h. over
f

p
f
rit.
cresc.
8

Our Director

March

F. E. Bigelow
Arranged by Henry Levine

Tempo di Marcia

mf
mp
mf
f
mf
1.
2.
ff
mf
The imitation Drum Solo, from ⊕ to ⊕, may be omitted.

⊛ If desired: omit repeat, and play next page.

ff
ff
sfz

Radetzky March

JOHANN STRAUSS

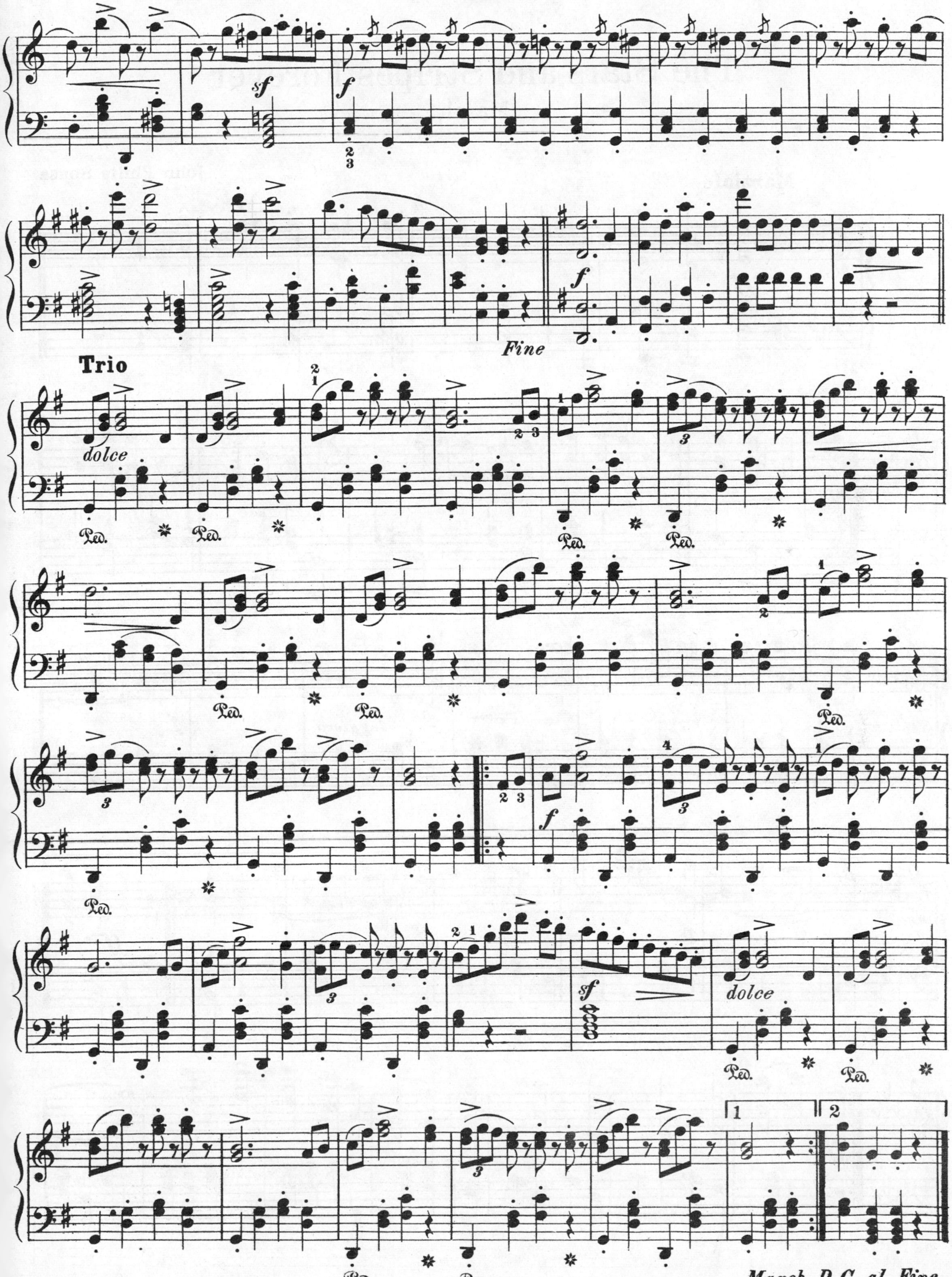
sf
f
Fine
Trio
dolce
f
sf
dolce
March D.C. al Fine

The Stars and Stripes Forever

March

John Philip Sousa

Marziale

ff
p
p

ff grandioso.
marcato il bassi

1
2

Under the Double Eagle
Unter dem Doppeladler

March

J. F. WAGNER. Op. 159

Introduction

ff basso marcato
1
2
ffz
ffz
ffz
ffz
Fine.
Trio.
pp
p dolcissimo
pp
p

pp
p
pp
ff energico
1
2
p
D. C. al Fine.

The Washington Post

March

John Philip Sousa

Tempo marziale

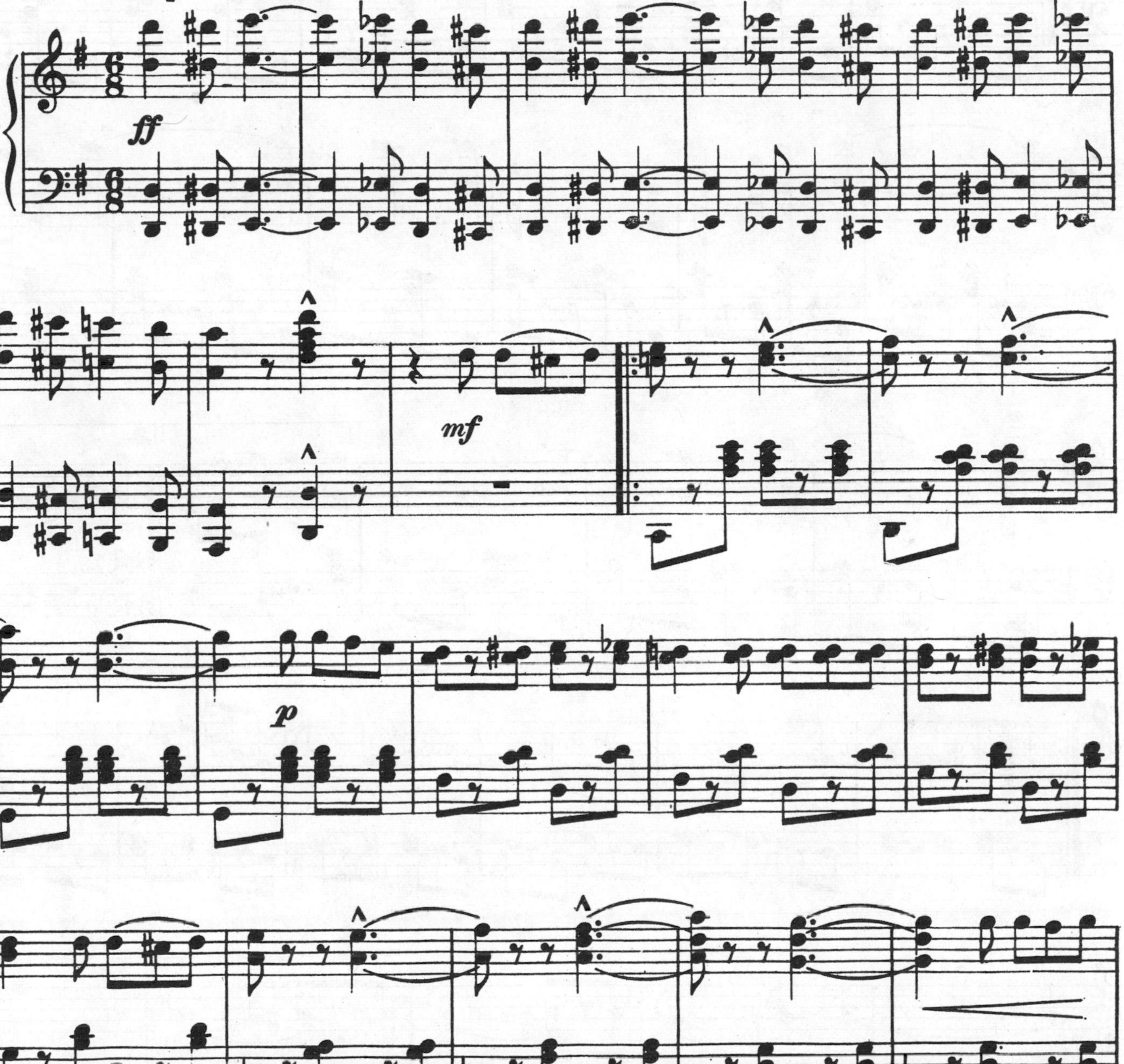

ff
1.
2.
p
1.
2.
ff

ff
ff
8
8
1.
2.
8

Wedding March
From "A Midsummer Night's Dream"

Revised and fingered by
KARL KLAUSER

F. Mendelssohn-Bartholdy

Allegro vivace

f
sf
1.
2.
tr

p
Ped.
p
Ped.
dim.
p
Ped.

cresc.
molto cresc.
sf
cresc.
ff sf
ff
Ped.
tr

tr
sf
ff
Ped.

Wien bleibt Wien

March

Johann Schrammel

Trio
p
p
ff
tr

Finale

Waves of the Danube

Donauwellen

J. IVANOVICI

Nº2
rit.
rit.
Fine

Nº 3
ff
p
dolce
1.
2.
p
f
Fine

No.4

FINALE

f
p
p
tr
tr
tr
f

Gold and Silver

Waltz

INTRODUCTION
Allegretto moderato

Franz Lehár

p
1
2
f
p
f
1
pp
2

mf
1
2
CODA
p
p
p
ri. . . . . tar. . . . dan. . do
p

a tempo
Prestissimo
ff

Artists' Life

Künstler-Leben

WALTZES

Johann Strauss

f
1.
2.
last time
p
D.S.
2
p
p
cresc.
f
pp
cresc.
f
pp
f
p
p
pp

pp
f
f
1.
f
p
p
pp
2.
last time
D.S.
3
p
p
f
f
tr
tr

1.
last time
D.S.
4
p
f
p
1.
f
2.

5
p
f
1.
2.
Coda
f
p
pp

f
tr
p
f
p
p
pp

pp
cresc.
5
3
1
fz
f
ff

On the Beautiful Blue Danube

An der schönen blauen Donau

Waltz. Johann Strauss. Op. 314

2.
mf
1.
f
p
2.
dol.
Close.
Fine.
dol.
pp
p
mf
Dal Segno senza repetizione al Fine.
3.
p
p cresc.
f
1.
p
2.
p
p

fz
1.
p
2.
p
Ending.
Intrada.
Waltz.
4.
f
p
p
1.
p
2.
fz
f
f
1.
f
2.
p
Ending.

Intrada.
5.
f
p
f
p
Waltz.
p
pp
1.
2.
p
f
f
f

1.
2.
ff
p
Coda.
p
cresc.
p
p
mf
f
p
f
pp
p

tr
f
p
Ped.

Ped.
ff
fz
fz
1
p
pp
dim.
cresc.
f

Tales from the Vienna Woods

Johann Strauss
Arranged by James Palmeri

ad lib.
rit.
a tempo

al Coda
1.
8 ad lib.
p
2.
mf
p rit.
a tempo
molto riten.
a tempo
1.
2.
poco più mosso

8 ad lib.
D. S. al Coda
Coda

Voices of Spring

Frühlingsstimmen

Waltz

Edited by Carl Deis

Johann Strauss, Op. 410

Ped.
p
cresc.
f
tr
1.
2.

f
mf
p dolce
cresc.
p
Ped.

p dolce
cresc.
f
p
cresc.
f
dim.
poco rit.
p
f a tempo

dim.
p
cresc.
f
p dolce
poco rit.
a tempo
mf
tr
Ped.

cresc.
dim.
Ped.

a tempo
f poco rit.
fz poco rit.
a tempo
Coda
f
f
mf
mf
p dolce
Ped.

mf
Ped.
p dolce
cresc.
p
Ped.
cresc.
tr
f
ff
Ped.
ff
fz

Estudiantina

Suite de Valses

Émile Waldteufel

Introduction
Tempo di Valse

Valse
Estudiantina *(Refrain)*

ff
p
1.
2.
f
Estudiantina (Couplet)
2
p espressivo
3
Fine

Chanson d'Automne

Jota de la Estudiantina

Tirana

1.
2.
f
D.S.
De Cadiz al Puerto
4
p
mf
Fine
El Tripili
ff ben marcato
D.S.

Coda
ff
mf
1.
2.
p
3

ff
ff
3
3

The Skaters
Les Patineurs
WALTZES

Émile Waldteufel

1.
2.
p
p
2
f risoluto
1.
2.
Sleigh-bells
p
1.
2.
f

espressivo
3
cresc.
dim.
1.
2.
p
grazioso
f
p

1.
2.
p
4
mf amabile
cresc. poco a poco
sf
p
1.
Fine
2.
mf
f
mf
f
mf
f
mf
f
mf
1.
mf
2.
ff
D. S.

Coda
ff risoluto
8
brillante
p
1.
2.
cresc.
f
ff
mf

f
mf
f
dim.
p
f
ff grandioso

311

Vienna Girls

WALTZ

C. M. Ziehrer. Op. 388

f rit.
a tempo
p
2
f
p
f
f
p

f
fp
fp
1.
2.
ff
3
f
rit.
p
a tempo
f

1.
2.
Coda
f
f
rit.
f

Andante
p
3
3
3
p
Animato
ff
p
f rit.

a tempo
p
p
p
p
p
f
p

ff
rit.
a tempo
p
f
f

Tango in D

Edited by Carl Deis

Isaac Albeniz, Op. 165, No. 2

molto rit.
poco meno
mf
p
mosso
pp
rit.
a tempo
mp
Tempo I°
pp
riten.
rit. molto

La Czarina

Mazurka russe

LOUIS GANNE

ff
sf
ff
pp
pp
ff
fff sec.
sec.
sec.
Drums
fff

Mazurka

ben marcato
ff
f Trumpets.
simile
ff (tutti.)
allarg.
a tempo
mf
f
ff
p
allarg.
a tempo

Trumpets
Ped.
simile
ff (tutti.)
Accompaniment very lightly (ad lib.)
Trio
sf

ff
mf
ff
mf cresc.
f
1
2
mf
D. C. (ad lib.)

Coda.
f
Ped.
Ped.
simile
ff
allargando
a tempo
mf
f
p
Ped.
mf

allarg.
a tempo
1
tr
2
mf
fff
animato
ff
sec.

Morris Dance

from "Henry VIII"

Edward German

Dance

f
Ped.
sf
pp 2d time f
p
1.
2.

ppp
Ped.
sf
sf
p
Ped.

mf
Ped.
Ped.
Ped.
f
Ped.
*
Ped.
*
Ped.
*
sf sf sf
Coda
Presto
ff
sf
sf
sf
Ped.
*

El Irresistible
Tango Argentino

L. Logatti
Arr. by G. J. S. W.

a tempo
poco rit.
p dolce
ff
ff
mf
p
pp
f

Con grazia

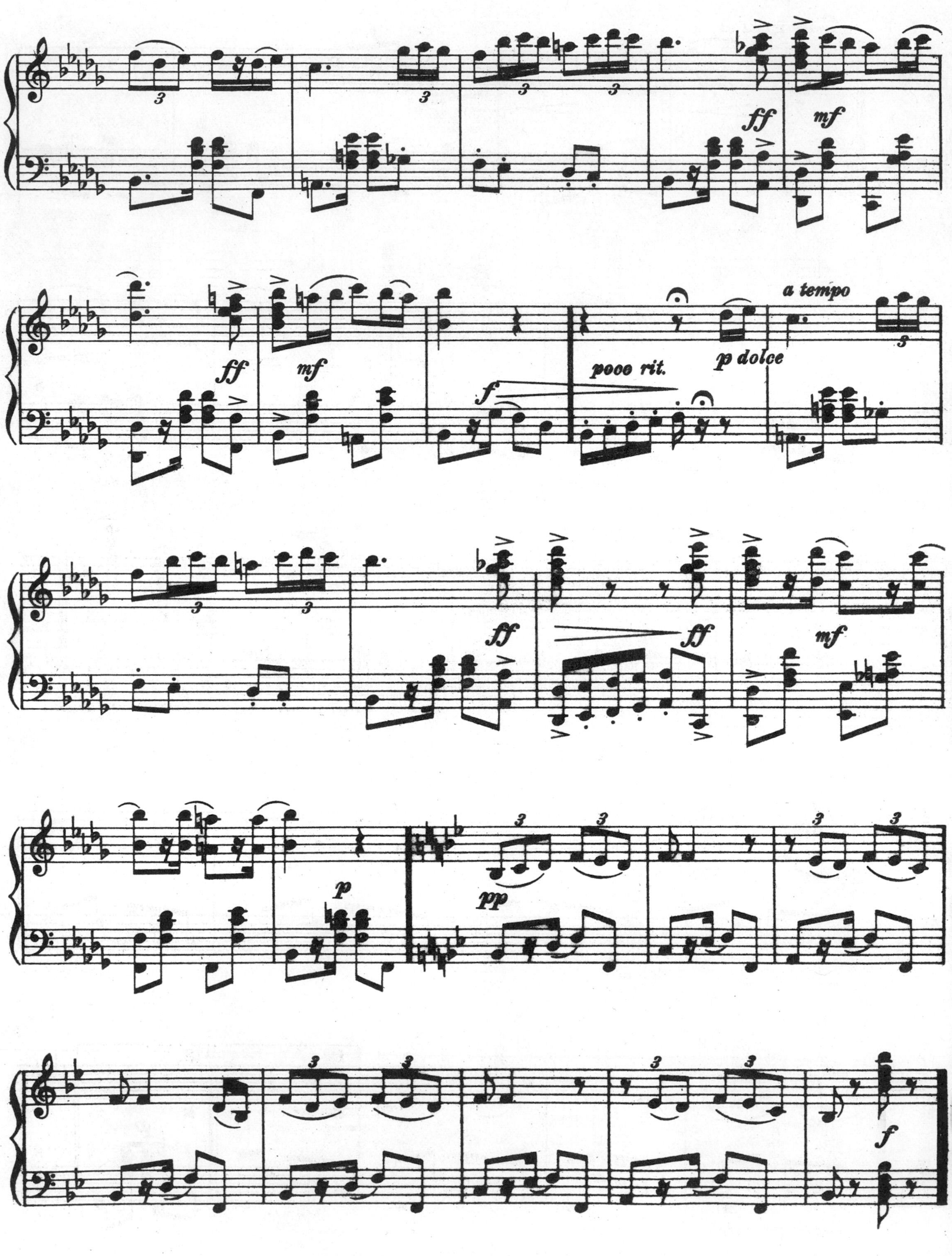
ff
mf
ff
mf
a tempo
poco rit.
p dolce
ff
ff
mf
p
pp
f

Dengozo

(Brazilian Maxixe-Tango)

Ernesto Nazareth
Arranged and edited by G. S. W.

Not too fast

1.
2.
senza ritard.
sfz sfz

Con grazia
p
sfz
mf
p
sfz
p
1.
2.
p
mf

1.
2.
leggiero
p
f
1.
2.
p
mf
senza ritard.
sfz sfz

Can-Can

from Light Opera "Orpheus in the Underworld"

Jacques Offenbach
Arranged by Henry Levine

1.
2.
p
f
sf

p
p
cresc.
ff
8
8

1.
2.
ff sempre
fff

The Wilhelmina Schottische

FRED. SCHILLING. 1862

f
f
Fine
p

f
p
1.
2.
D. S. al Fine.

Y... Como Le Vá?

Tango Argentino

On Motives by H. Herpin

J. Valverde

f

L'esprit Français

Polka

Émile Waldteufel

poco a poco cresc.
m.s.
scherzando
f
p
ben marcato
ff
p poco a poco cresc.
m. s.

f
p
p
f
Trio
p
leggiero
p
ff
sonore
pp

Coda
poco a poco cresc.
m.s.

College Hornpipe

Fisher's Hornpipe

Johnny's Made a Wedding o'it

Highland Fling

Garry Owen

Jig

Miss Mc Leod's Reel

Paddy Whack

Jig

The White Cockade

St. Patrick's Day

The Campbells are Coming

The Irish Washerwoman

Country Gardens

Turkey in the Straw

Turtle-Dove
Lachtäubchen
Polka badine

Franz Behr. Op. 303
Arranged by Rob. Schaab

Allegretto grazioso

SECONDO

361

Turtle-Dove

Lachtäubchen

Polka badine

PRIMO

Franz Behr. Op. 303
Arranged by Rob. Schaab

mf
Ped.
cresc.
f
1.
2.
p
fz
1
rit.

PRIMO

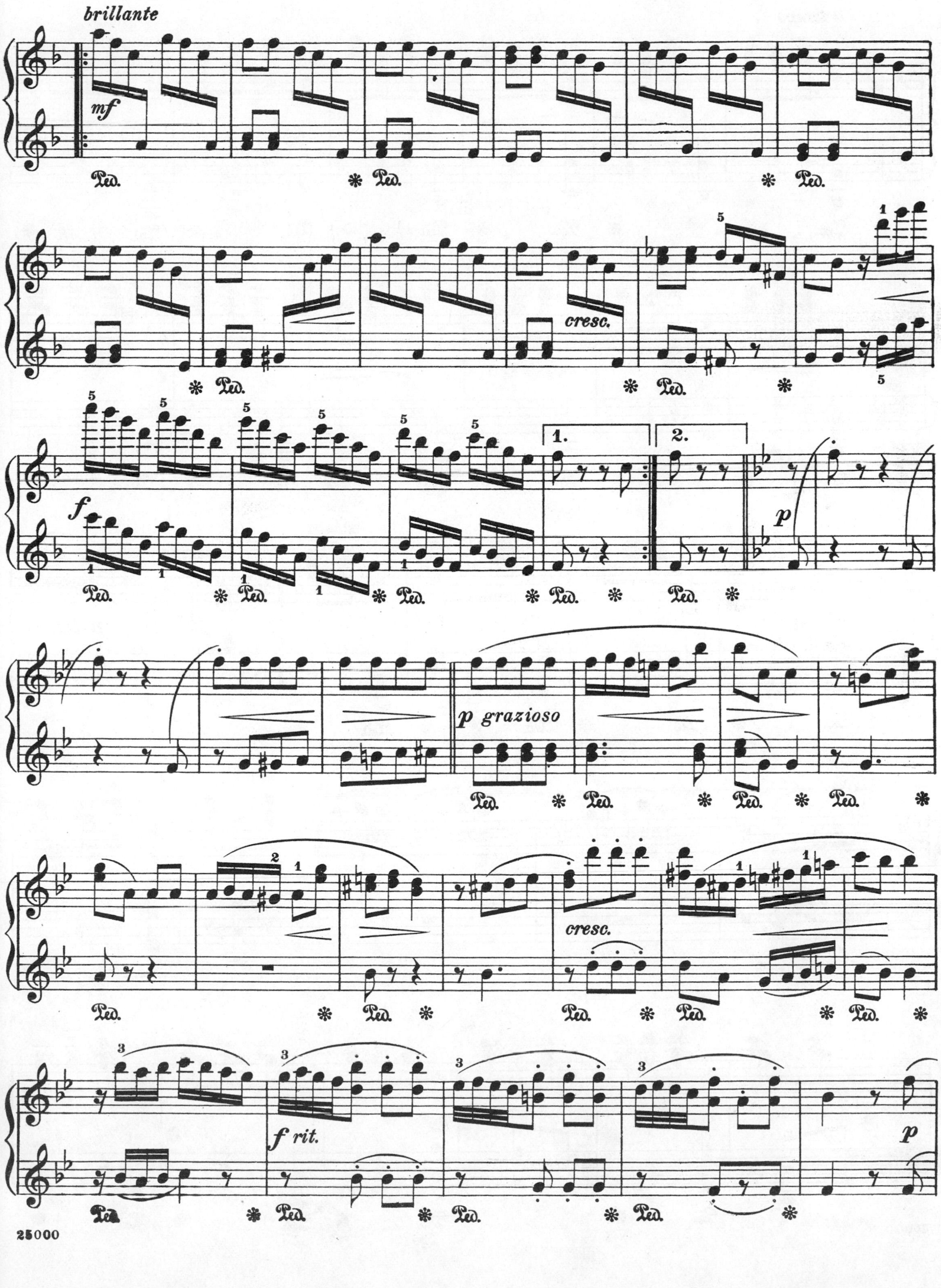
brillante
mf
cresc.
f
1.
2.
p
p grazioso
cresc.
f rit.
p

a tempo
p
Ped.
*
cresc.
f rit.
a tempo
p legg.
p legg.
mf

PRIMO

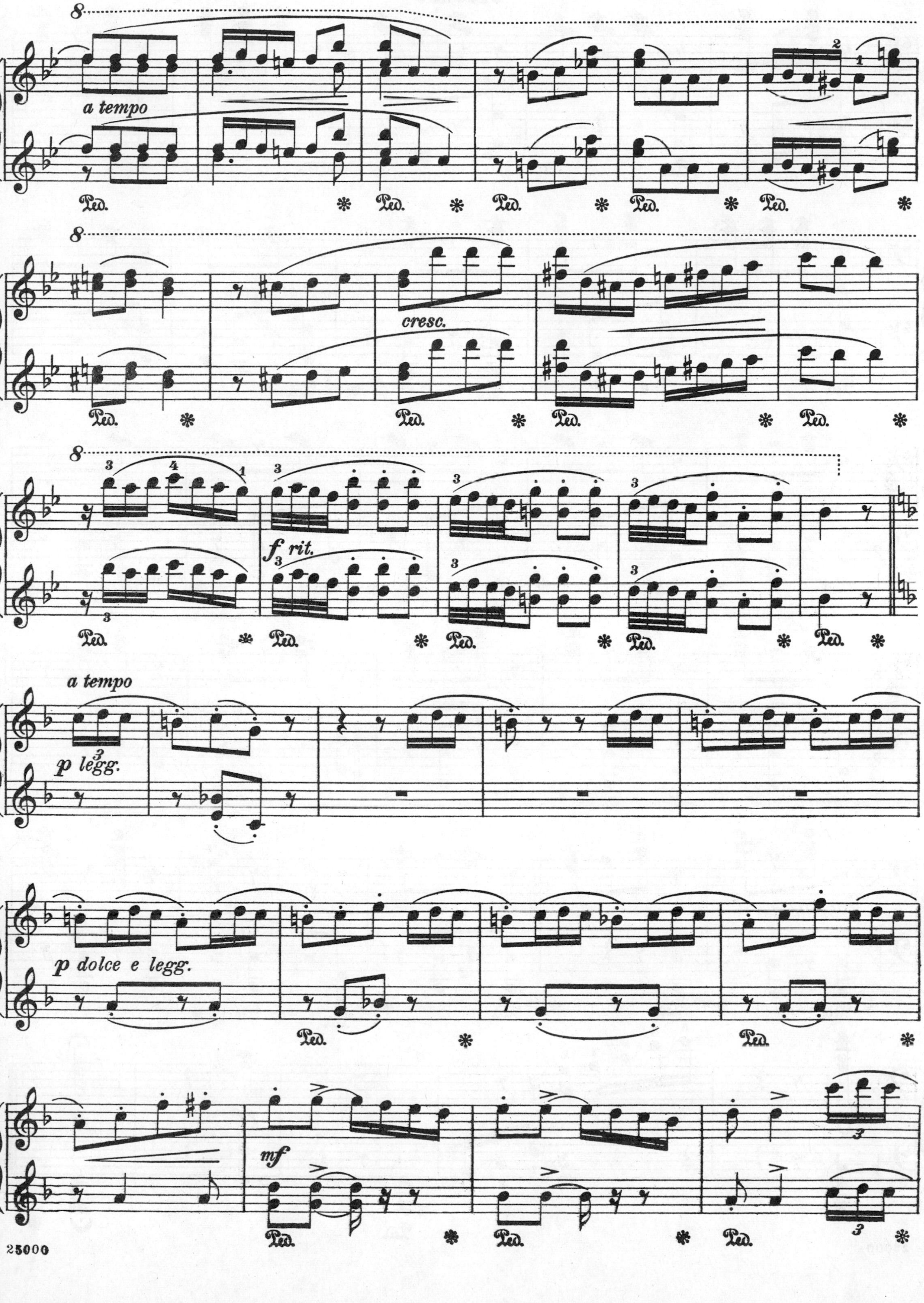
a tempo
cresc.
f rit.
a tempo
p legg.
p dolce e legg.
mf
Ped.

SECONDO

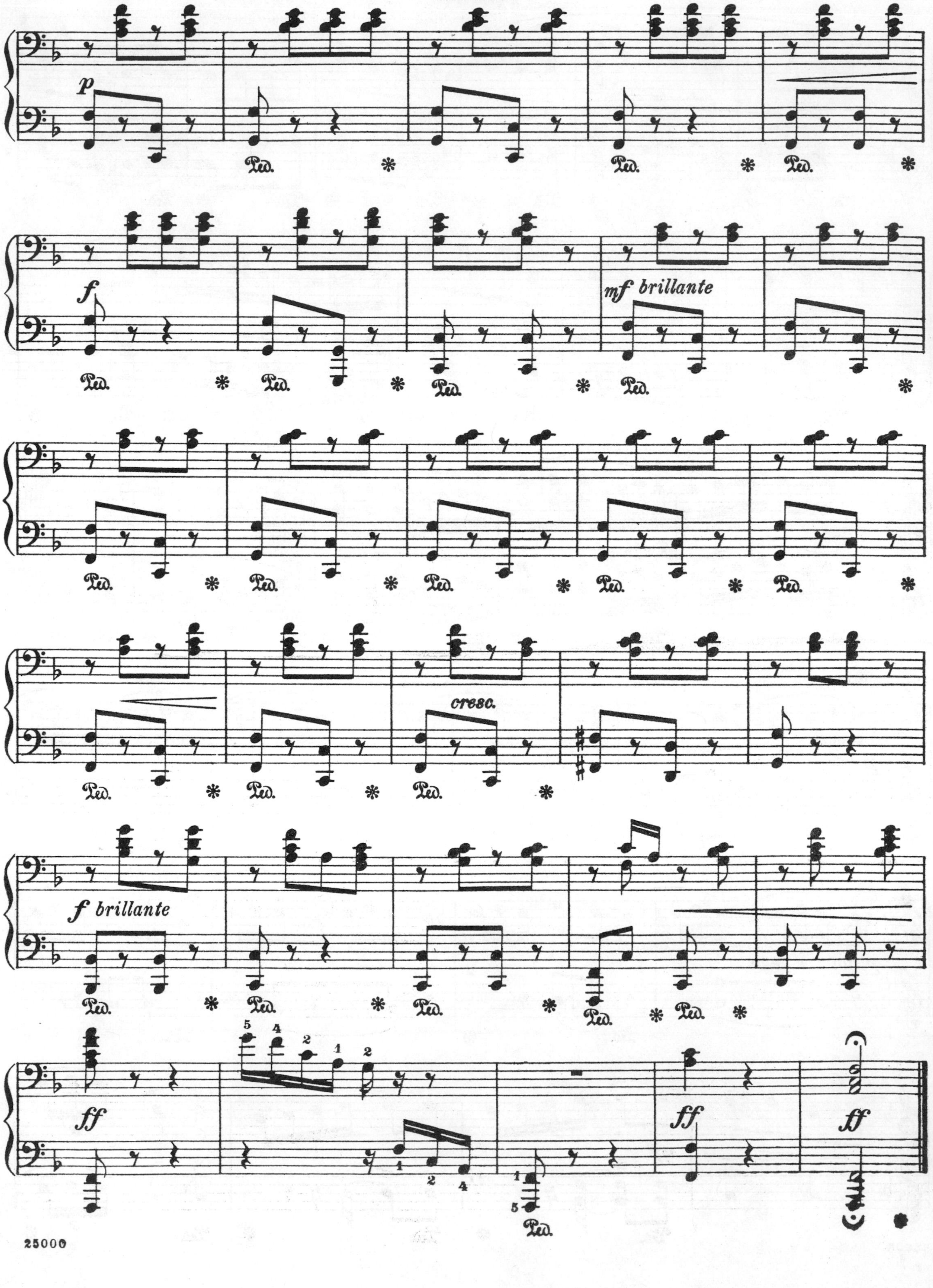
p
Ped.
f
mf brillante
cresc.
f brillante
ff

p
f
brillante
mf
cresc.
f brillante
ff
ff
Ped.

Theme from Concerto in A Minor

Edvard Grieg, Op. 16
Arranged by Antonio Lora

SECONDO

Theme from Concerto in A Minor

Edvard Grieg, Op. 16
Arranged by Antonio Lora

PRIMO

pp
rit.
Ped.
a tempo
l.h.
p
cresc.
simile
Meno allegro
rit.
p
dolce
tranquillo e cantabile
p
pp
pp

dim.
mf ritard.
pp
a tempo
cresc.
Meno allegro
p
rit.
tranquillo e cantabile
mp
mf
f
pp
sosten.

SECONDO

animato
p
Ped.
cre
scen
do
dim.
sosten.
mp
sempre più animato
col Ped.
poco rit.
f vivo

PRIMO

animato
p cantabile
cre -
scen - - do
dim. sosten.
mf sempre più animato
8
poco rit.
ff vivo

SECONDO

ff
stretto
Ped.
fz
fz
fz
fz
fz
fz
fz
fz
fz
Ped.
l.h.
fz
cresc.
fz
rall.
Tempo I
fff
Ped.
Ped.
Ped.
Ped.
Ped.
Ped.
simile
Ped.

PRIMO

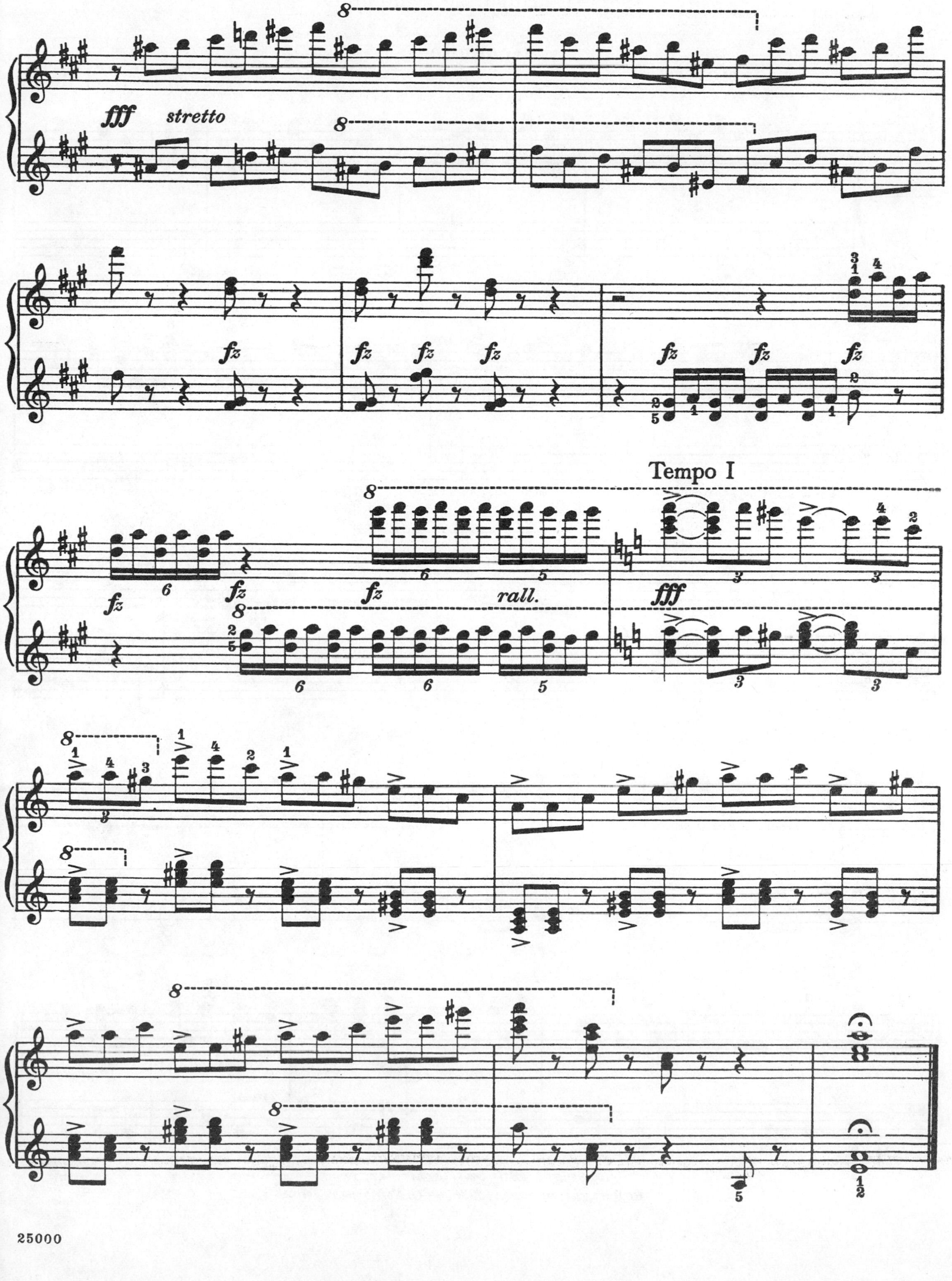

fff
stretto
fz
rall.
Tempo I
fff

Andante
from the Surprise Symphony

Secondo

Andante

Josef Haydn

Andante
from the Surprise Symphony

Primo

Andante

Josef Haydn

Aragonaise

from the Ballet "Le Cid"

Edited and fingered by
Louis Oesterle

Secondo

J. MASSENET

Aragonaise

from the Ballet "Le Cid"

Edited and fingered by
Louis Oesterle

Primo

Allegro brillante

J. MASSENET

Secondo

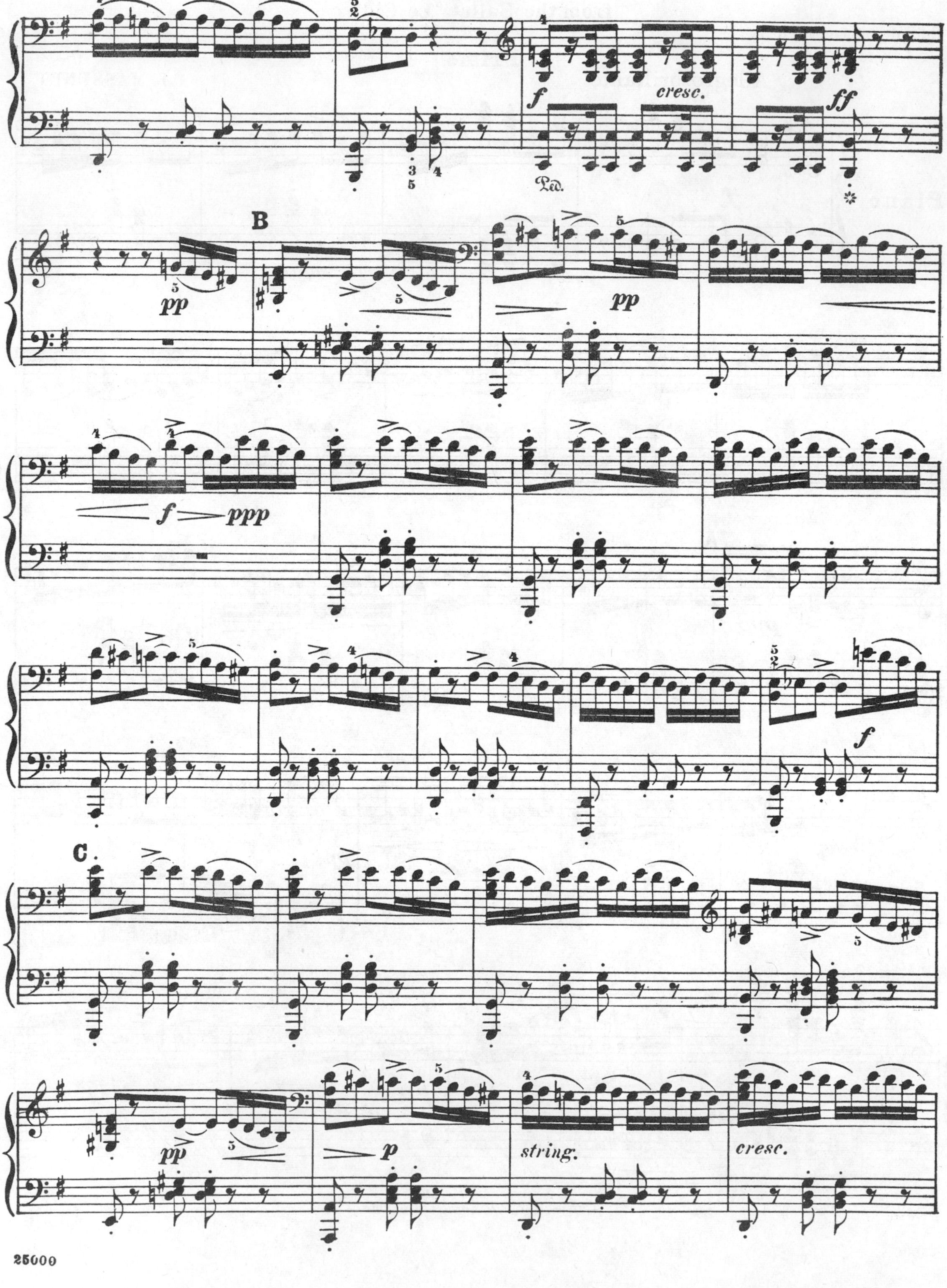
B
C
pp
pp
ppp
cresc.
string.
Ped.

Primo

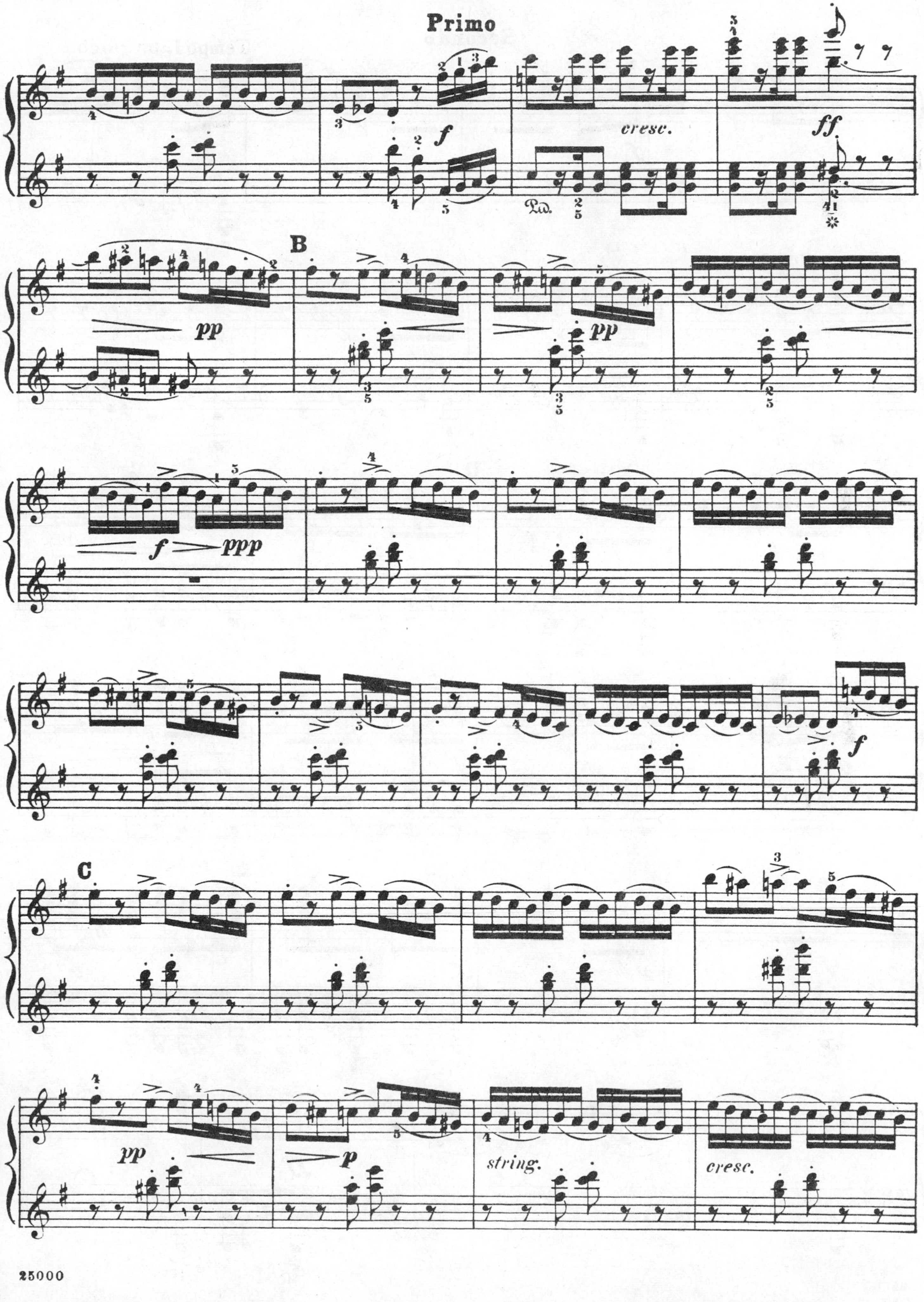

Primo
f
cresc.
ff
B
pp
pp
f
ppp
f
C
pp
p
string.
cresc.

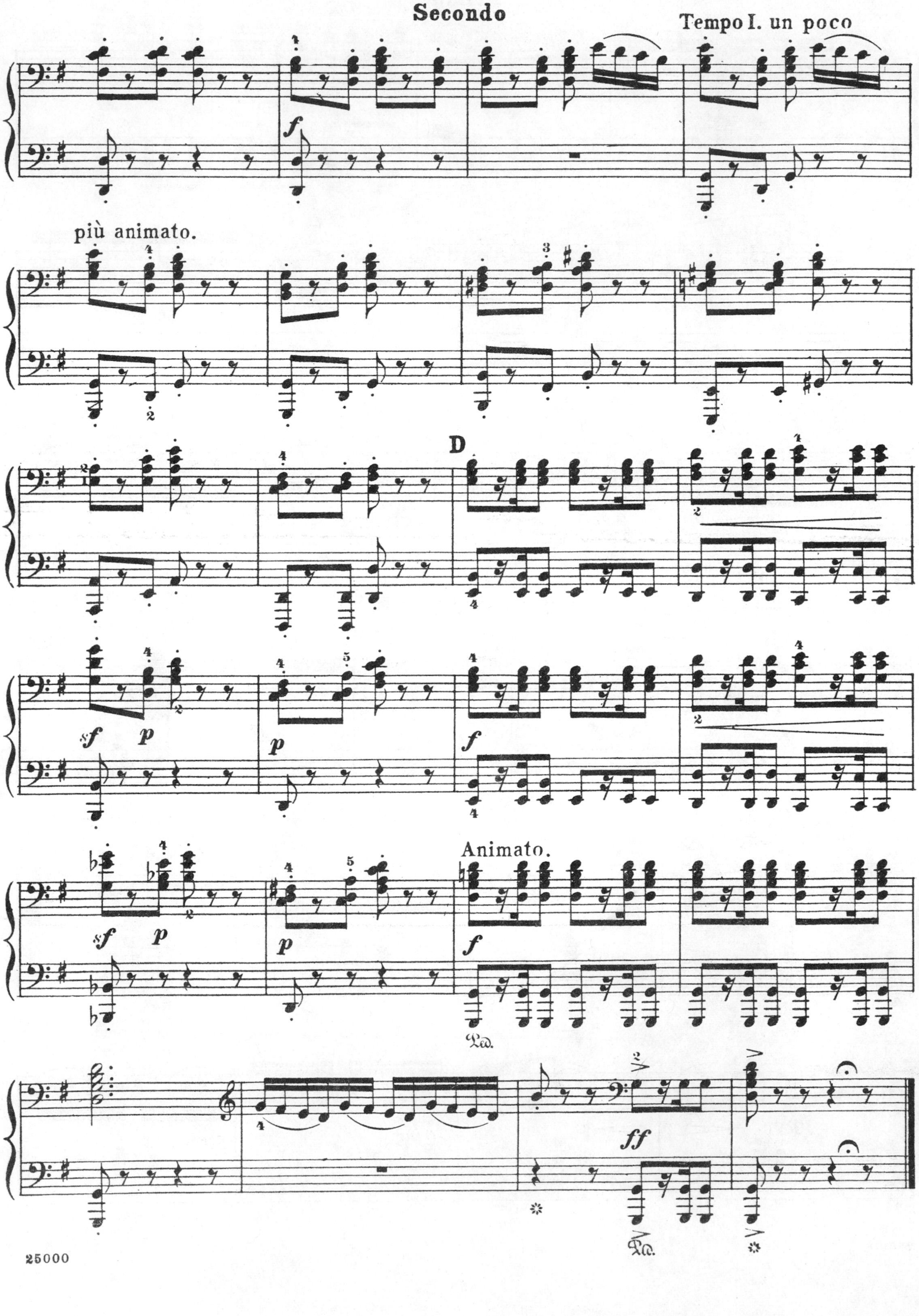
Secondo
Tempo I. un poco
più animato.
D
Animato.

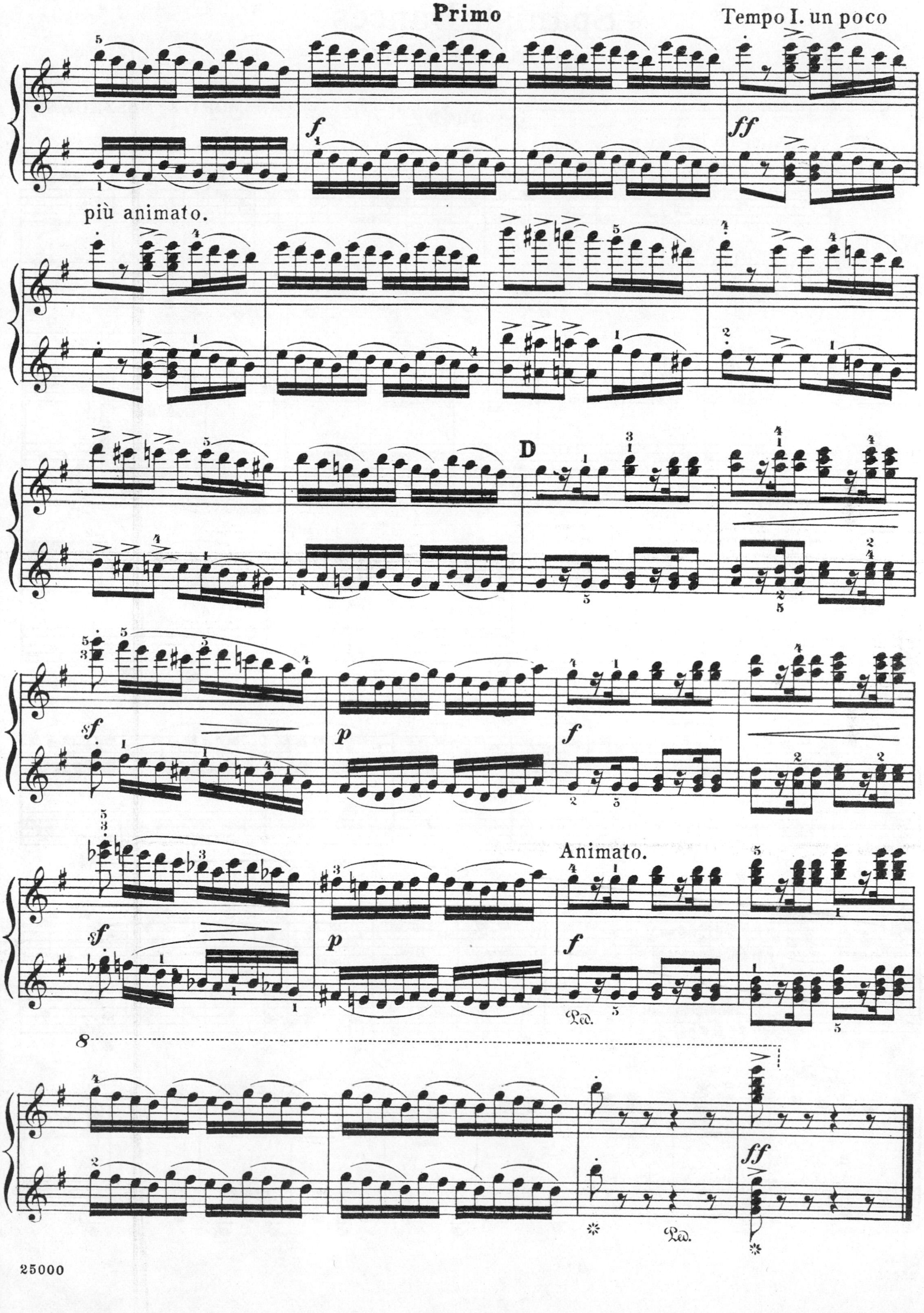
Primo
Tempo I. un poco
più animato.
D
Animato.
8

Spanish Dances
Spanische Tänze

Revised and fingered by
Wm Scharfenberg

Secondo

MORITZ MOSZKOWSKI

Allegro brioso

No 1.

Spanish Dances
Spanische Tänze

Revised and fingered by
Wm. Scharfenberg

Primo

MORITZ MOSZKOWSKI

Allegro brioso

Secondo

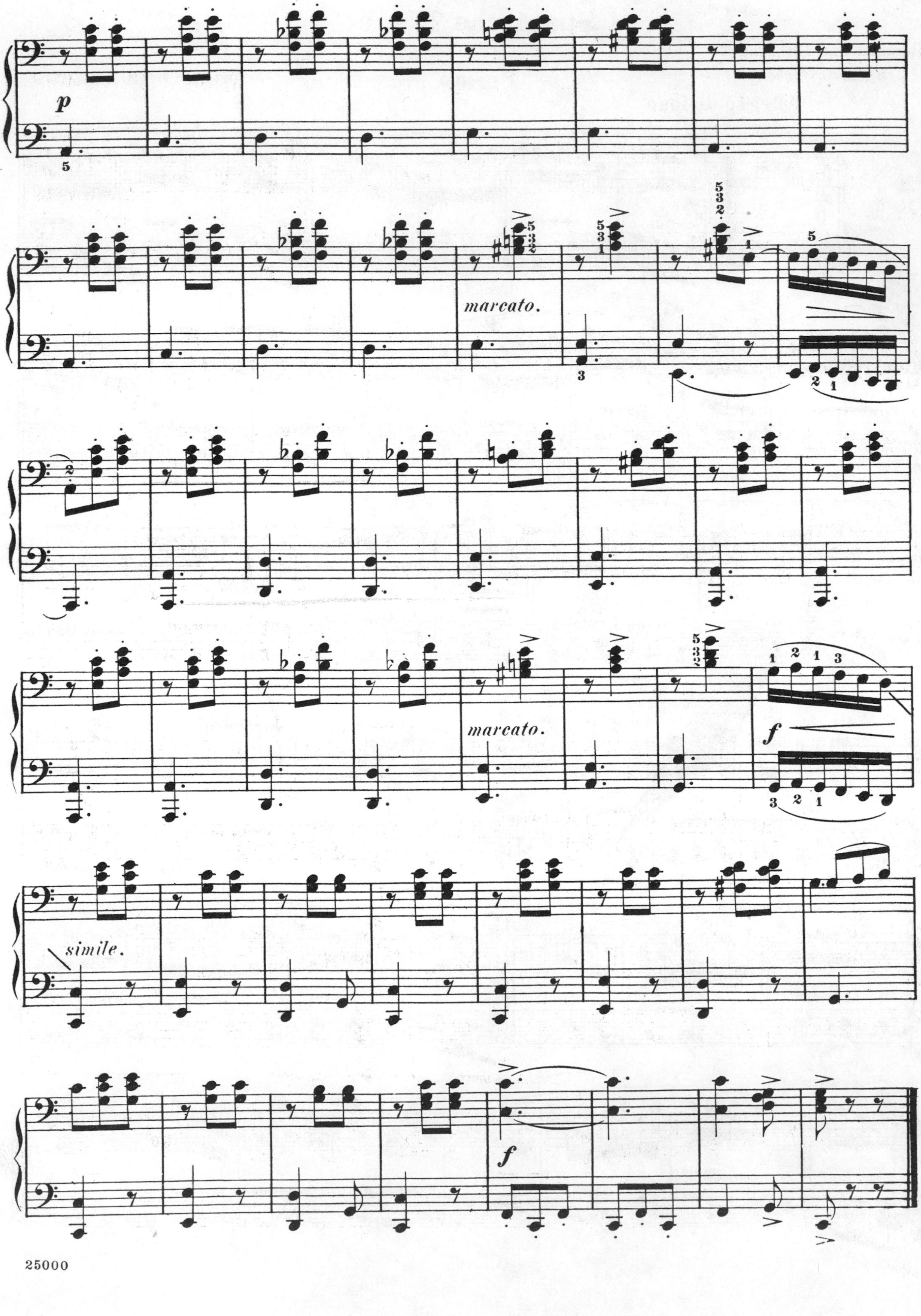
p
marcato.
marcato.
f
simile.
f

Primo

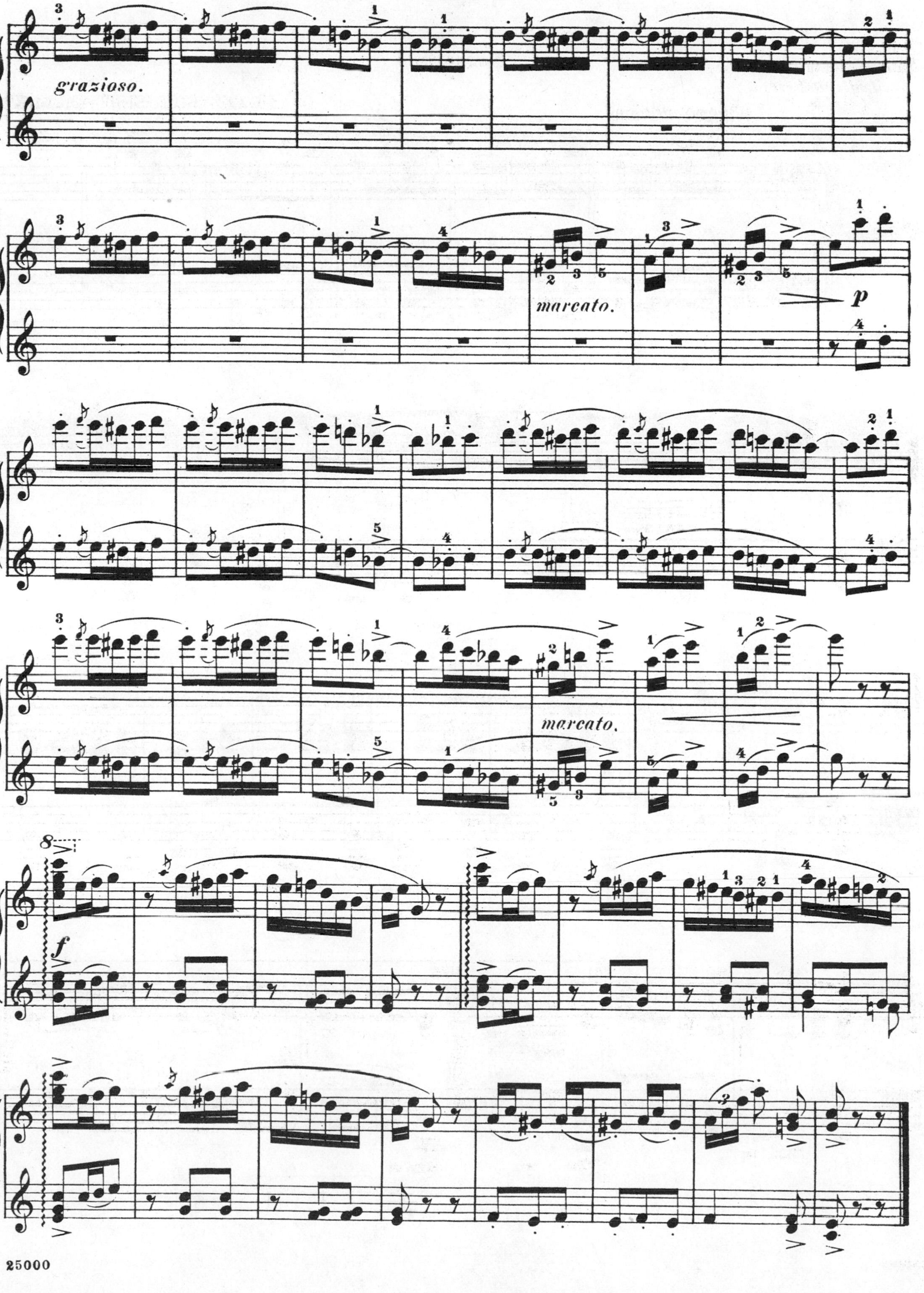
grazioso.
marcato.
p
marcato.
f

Military March

Edited and fingered by
Louis Oesterle

Secondo

FRANZ SCHUBERT. Op. 51, No. 1

Allegro vivace

Military March

Primo

Edited and fingered by
Louis Oesterle

FRANZ SCHUBERT. Op. 51, № 1

Allegro vivace

Secondo

Primo

Secondo

Trio
p
simile stacc.
cresc.
p
p
cresc.
p
cresc.
Marcia da Capo

Trio **Primo**

Marcia da Capo

Opening Theme from Piano Concerto No. 1

Peter Ilyich Tchaikovsky
Arranged by Antonio Lora

SECONDO

Andante non troppo e molto maestoso

Opening Theme from Piano Concerto No.1

Peter Ilyich Tchaikovsky
Arranged by Antonio Lora

PRIMO

Andante non troppo e molto maestoso

SECONDO

PRIMO

Entr'acte-Gavotte
from
"Mignon"

Edited and fingered by
Louis Oesterle

Secondo

Allegretto (♩=76)

AMBROISE THOMAS

Entr'acte-Gavotte

from

"Mignon"

Edited and fingered by
Louis Oesterle

Allegretto (♩= 76) **Primo** AMBROISE THOMAS

25000

Secondo

Primo

Secondo

Primo

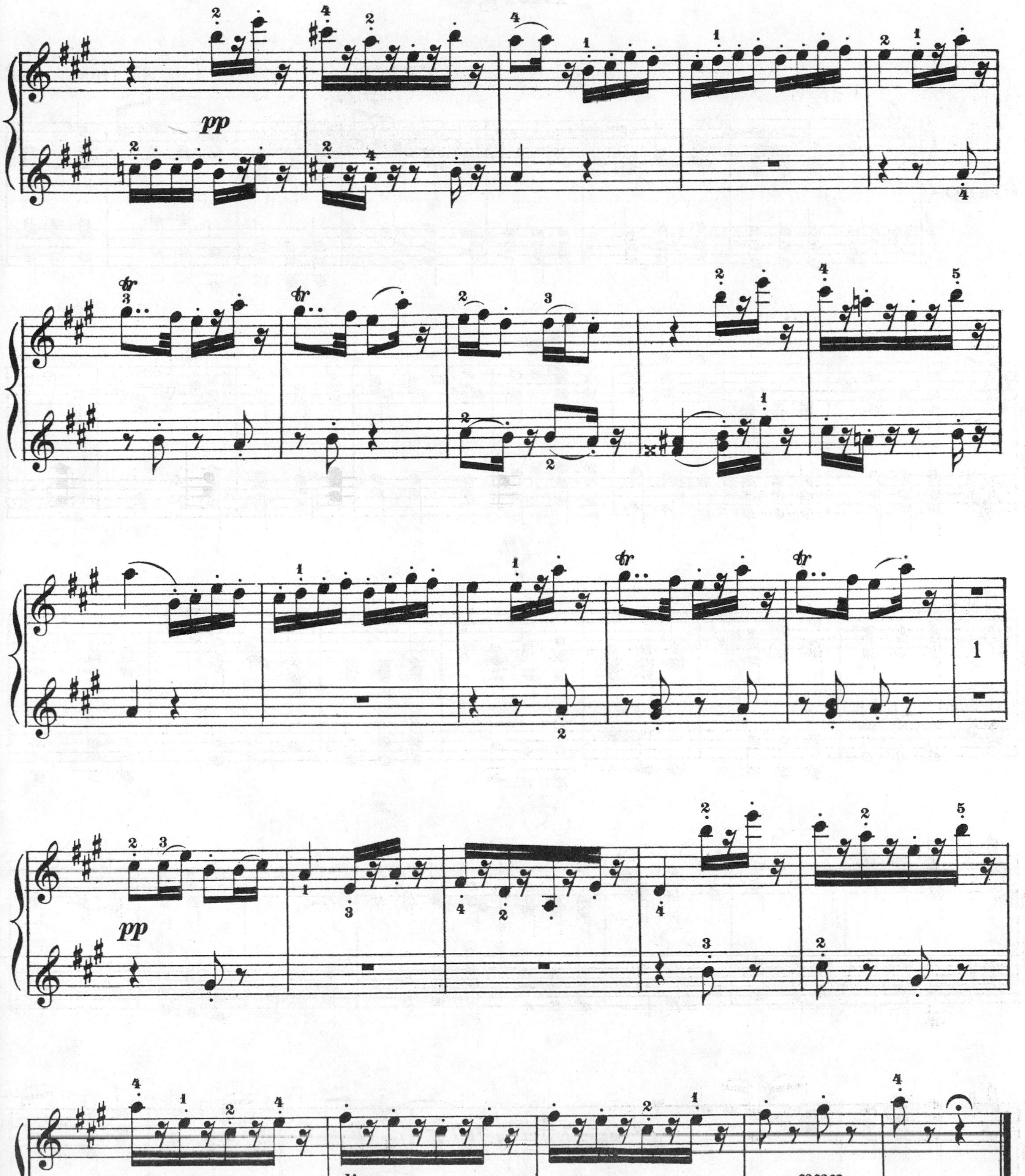
pp
tr
pp
dim.
ppp

Largo

Händel
(1685-1759)

f
p
3
cresc.
f
rit.
Ave Maria
Arcadelt
(1490-1557?)
Andante
p
mf
cresc.
mf
cresc.
f
ff
p
f
p
f
p
dim.
pp

Meditation

On the First Prelude by J. S. Bach

By CHARLES GOUNOD

Transcribed for Piano
by the Arranger

Andante semplice
Piano
p

il canto ben marcato e legato (con sentimento contemplativo)

pp

cresc.

p

cresc.

p

cresc.
dim.
p
cresc.
dim.
p
cresc.
dim.
p
cresc.
f
dim.
p
cresc. molto
Ped.

f
dim.
p
cresc. molto
f
più f
tutta forza
molto maestoso

ben marcato
ff
p
pp
Ped.
cresc.
p
cresc.
p
cresc.
dim.
p

cresc.
dim.
p
cresc.
dim.
p
cresc.
cresc.
f
dim.
p
cresc. molto
8
loco
Ped.

f
cresc. molto
più f
tutta forza
loco
fff
molto maestoso
ff
dim.
rit.
p
Ped.

Lamb of God
(Agnus Dei)

Georges Bizet
Transcribed by Rob Roy Peery

simile
f
dim.
p
cresc.
f
p

mf
cresc. molto
ff
p
f
ff allargando
f
p
ff molto ritard.

Panis Angelicus
(O Bread of Life)

César Franck
Transcribed by Rob Roy Peery

Poco lento

mf
simile
mp
cresc.
f
p
f

mf
rit.
mf a tempo
cresc.
f
dim.
mf

cresc.
f
ff
dim.
rall.
l.h.
p a tempo
rall. e dim.
pp

Hallelujah! from "The Messiah"

G. F. HANDEL.

Allegretto moderato.

marc.
marc.
r.h.
tr
tr
Ped.
Ped.
Ped.

Ped.
f

f
Ped.
ff
Ped.
Ped.

Consolation

F. Mendelssohn

Adagio non troppo (♩= 58)

CHORD ORGAN

Emperor Waltz

JOHANN STRAUSS

2 = C
1 = F 3 = G7

Valsette

Felix Borowski
Moderato
Lowest Manual Key is
NC
G
Am
D7
A7
C
F7
E7
G7
B7
Dm7
Fine
D. S. al Fine
2 = G
1 = C 3 = D7

Waltz

from "Faust"

CHARLES GOUNOD

Tempo di Valse

2 = C	
1 = F	3 = G7

The Sleeping Beauty

Waltz

P. I. Tchaikovsky, Op. 66, No. 6

Tempo di Valse

2 = C
1 = F 3 = G7

Chanson Triste

P. I. Tchaikovsky

FLAT
Square Notes

2 = B♭
1 = E♭ 3 = F7

Kentucky Babe

ADAM GEIBEL

Richard Henry Buck

Moderato
Lowest Manual Key is
Skeet-ers am a-hum-min' on de hon-ey-suck-le vine, Sleep, Kentuck-y Babe!
Sand-man am a-com-in' to dis lit-tle babe of mine, Sleep, Ken-tuck-y Babe!
Sil-v'ry moon am shin-in' in de haeb-ens up a-bove, Bob-o-link am pin-in' fo' his
lit-tle la-dy love, You is might-y luck-y, Babe of old Ken-tuck-y,
Close yo' eyes in sleep. Fly a-way, fly a-way, Ken-tuck-y Babe,
fly a-way to rest, Fly a-way, Lay yo' kink-y, wool-y head on yo' mam-my's breast.
Um Um close yo' eyes in sleep.

2 = C
1 = F 3 = G7

Mattinata

Ruggiero Leoncavallo

Allegretto

FLAT Square Notes

2 = F
1 = B♭ 3 = C7

Evening Prayer

"When At Night I Go To Sleep"

from "Hansel and Gretel"

E. Humperdinck

Largo assai
Lowest Manual Key is
C F G C
2 1 3mj 2
When at night I go to sleep, Four-teen an-gels
G Dm C F G7 C
3mj 4m 2 1 3 2
watch do keep, Two my head are guard - ing,
C7 Dm A7 Dm Bb7 Eb
27 4m 5 4m Bb7 Eb
Two my feet are guid - ing, Two are on my
C7 F D7 G D- Am C7 F
27 1 4 3mj 4- 5m 27 1
right hand, Two are on my left hand, Two who warm-ly
C Gm Dm F C
2 3m 4m 1 2
cov - er, Two who o'er me hov - er, Two to whom 'tis
D7 C Em Am Fm G7 C
4 2 6m 5m 1m 3 2
giv - en To guide my steps to heav - - en.
2 = C
1 = F 3 = G7

The Spacious Firmament

Arr. by J. M. HANERT

Joseph Haydn

Firmly, with authority

The spa - cious fir - ma - ment on high With all the
blue e - the - real sky And span - gled heav'ns, a shin - ing
frame, Their great o - ri - gi - nal pro - claim. Th'un - wea - ried sun from
day to day Doth his Cre - a - tor's pow'r dis - play And
pub - lish - es to ev - 'ry land The work of an Al - might - y Hand.

FLAT
Square Notes

2 = B♭
1 = E♭ 3 = F7

Sometimes I Feel Like a Motherless Chile

Arr. by J. M. HANERT

Negro Spiritual

Andante

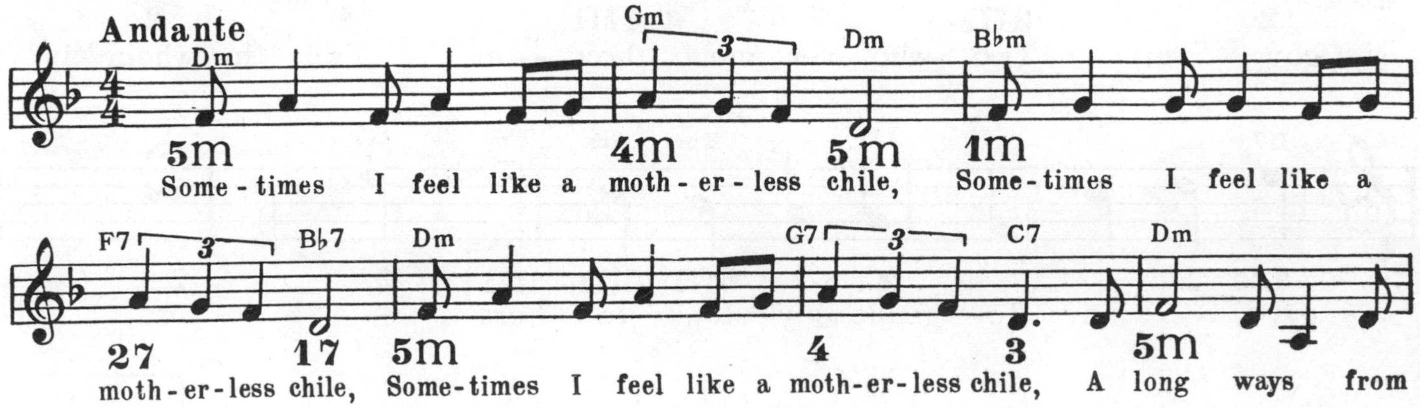

2 = F
1 = B♭ 3 = C7

B♭7 Dm A7 Dm
17 5m 6 5m
home, A long ways from home. Some-times I feel like a
Gm 3 Dm B♭m F7 3 B♭7 Dm
4m 5m 1m 27 17 5m
moth-er-less chile, Some-times I feel like a moth-er-less chile, Some-times I feel like a
G7 3 C7 Dm B♭7 Dm A7 Dm
4 3 5m 17 5m 6 5m
moth-er-less chile, A long ways from home, A long ways from home.

Steal Away

Arr. by J. M. HANERT

Negro Spiritual

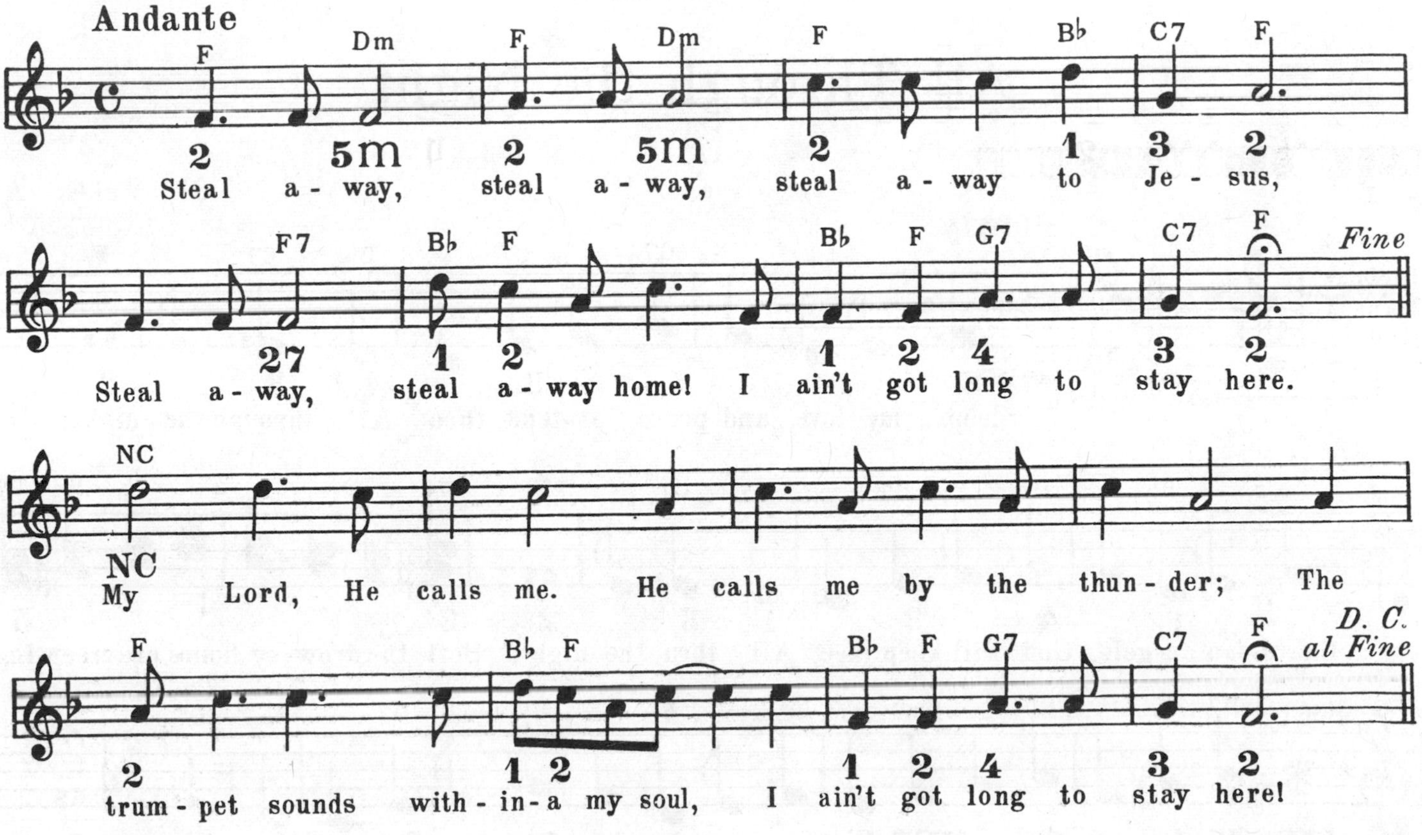
Andante
F Dm F Dm F B♭ C7 F
2 5m 2 5m 2 1 3 2
Steal a-way, steal a-way, steal a-way to Je-sus,
F7 B♭ F B♭ F G7 C7 F Fine
27 1 2 1 2 4 3 2
Steal a-way, steal a-way home! I ain't got long to stay here.
NC
NC
My Lord, He calls me. He calls me by the thun-der; The
F B♭ F B♭ F G7 C7 F D. C. al Fine
2 1 2 1 2 4 3 2
trum-pet sounds with-in-a my soul, I ain't got long to stay here!

2 = F	
1 = B♭	3 = C7

The Sweetest Story Ever Told

R. M. Stults

Espressivo
Lowest Manual Key is
Tell me, do you love me? Tell me soft-ly, sweet-ly, as of old! Tell me that you
love me, For that's the sweet-est sto-ry ev-er told. Tell me, do you love me? Whisper softly,
sweet-ly, as of old; Tell me that you love me, For that's the sweetest sto-ry ev-er told.

FLAT
Square Notes

2 = F
1 = B♭ 3 = C7

All Through the Night

Old Welsh Air

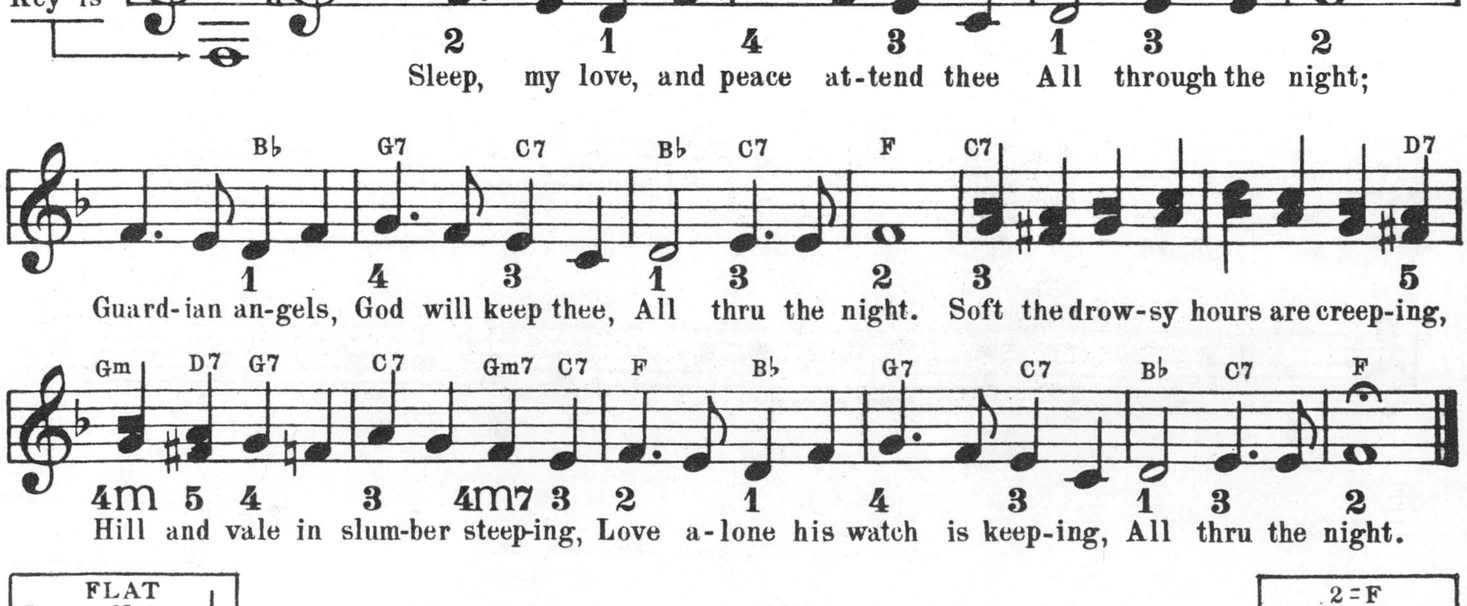
Slowly
Lowest Manual Key is
Sleep, my love, and peace at-tend thee All through the night;
Guard-ian an-gels, God will keep thee, All thru the night. Soft the drow-sy hours are creep-ing,
Hill and vale in slum-ber steep-ing, Love a-lone his watch is keep-ing, All thru the night.

FLAT
Square Notes

2 = F
1 = B♭ 3 = C7

HAMMOND ORGAN

Cadiz

Spinet Registration

Upper (U) - - - 67 7476 354

Lower [L] - - - 5464 4433

Pedal - - - 3 (or 4)

Tablets - - - 1234567

↓↓↑↓↓↓↓

Pre-Set Model Registration

Upper (A♯) - - - 47 5876 354

Lower [A♯] - - - 00 4353 444

Pedal - - - 43

Vibrato 3

I. Albeniz

Arr. by Fred Feibel

cresc.
f
mf
rit.
a tempo

poco rit.
mf
a tempo
rit
p
a tempo
rit
8va
mf
a tempo
8
poco rall.
a tempo
mf

To Coda
L
Both hands

p
mf
p
mf
U
f
p
D.S. al
Coda
molto cresc.
ff

Largo

From the "New World" Symphony

(U) 00 5724 340
[L] 5444 3000
Ped. 3

Antonin Dvořák
Arranged by Stephen J. Baranoski

f
p
pp
p
U
00 5720 000
cresc.
sf
L
ff
L
fff
pp
U
cresc.
U
dim.
p
L

L
dim.
pp
U
ppp
L 5484 2000
cresc.
f
p
U
L 5404 2000
mp
f
U
p
pp

Songs My Mother Taught Me

(U) 00 5444 122
[L] 5462 3000
Ped. 3

Antonin Dvořák
Arranged by Stephen J. Baranoski

Andante con moto

U 00 5844 122
L
3
3
f
dim.
pp
L

He shall feed His flock

(From "The Messiah")

George Frederic Handel

* Spinet

2.
mf
A#
U
p
A#
L
cresc.
f
mp

Whispering Hope

(U) 20 7535 244
[L] 7544 2121
Ped. 4

Alice Hawthorne
Arranged by Stephen J. Baranoski

Moderato

Refrain
U
L 7548 2121
D. C.
L 7544 2121
D. C.

God so loved the world

(From "The Crucifixion")

Hammond Organ

Upper (A#) 00 5634 210
Lower [A#] 00 6432 210
Pedal 4-3
Vibrato I

Spinet Model

Upper (U) 00 5634 210
Lower [L] 6432 2110
Pedal 3
Normal Vibrato

Sir John Stainer

* Spinet

p
mf
p

A♯
U
p
A♯
L
mp
mf

cresc.
mf
rall. e dim.
p a tempo
pp
rall.

Were You There?

Hammond Organ
Lower [A#] 00 6634 211
Pedal 4-3
Vibrato II or ½ Trem.

Spinet Model
Lower [L] 6634 2110
Pedal 3
Normal Vibrato

Negro Spiritual

* Spinet

rit.
mp
a tempo
mf
mf
mp
(♮)
rit.

After The Ball

Words and Music by
CHAS. K. HARRIS

Valse moderato

f
rall.
VOICE
p
A little maiden climbed an old man's knee, Begged for a story, "Do Uncle please," Why are you
Bright lights were flashing in the grand ballroom, Softly the music, playing sweet tunes, There came my
Long years have passed, child I've never wed, True to my lost love, though she is dead, She tried to

sin - gle, why live a - lone?
sweet - heart my love my own,
tell me, tried to ex - plain,
Have you no ba - bies, have you no
I wish some wa - ter; leave me a -
I would not list - en, plead - ings were
home?
lone!
vain,
I had a sweet - heart, years,
When I re - turned dear, there
One day a let - ter came,
years a - go;
stood a man,
from that man,
Where she is now pet,
Kiss - ing my sweet - heart
He was her broth - er

you will soon know. List to the stor - y, I'll tell it, all, I be - lieved her faith - less, af - ter the ball.
as lov - ers can. Down fell the glass pet, brok - en that's all, Just as my heart was, af - ter the ball.
the let - ter ran. That's why I'm lone - ly, no home at all, I broke her heart pet, af - ter the ball.
CHORUS
After the ball is o - ver, Af - ter the break of morn,

After the danc-ers leav-ing, After the stars are
gone; Man-y a heart is ach-ing, if you could
read them all; Man-y the hopes that have van-ished,
Af-ter the ball.
1
2.
ball.

Aloha Oe

Farewell to Thee

Moderato

Composed by H. M. QUEEN LILIUOKALANI

p solo
Ha - a - heo ka u - a i - na pa - li Ke
Proud - ly swept the rain - cloud by the cliff As
p
nihi a - e - la ka - na - he - le E ha - ha - i a - na i - ka
on it glid - ed through the trees, Still fol - low - ing with grief the
li - ko Pu - a a - hi - hi le - hu - a - o u - ka.
li - ko The a - hi - hi - le - hua of the vale.

CHORUS.
ff
A - lo - ha oe, a - lo - ha oe, E ke o - na-o - na no - ho i - ka li - po A
Fare-well to thee, fare-well to thee, Thou charm-ing one who dwellst a-mong the bow - ers; One
ff
ff
fond em-brace a ho - i a - e au Un - til we meet a - gain.
fond em-brace be - fore I now de - part, Un - til we meet a - gain.

2.

Ka halia ko aloha kai hiki mai
Ke hone ae nei i ku'u manawa
O oe no ka'u aloha
A loko e hana nei.

3.

Maopopo kuu ike ika nani
Na pua rose o Maunawili
I laila hoohie na mau u
Mikiala ika nani oia pua.

2.

Thus sweet memories come back to me,
Bringing fresh remembrance of the past;
Dearest one, yes thou art mine own,
From thee true love shall ne'er depart.

3.

I have seen and watched thy loveliness,
Thou sweet rose of Maunawili,
And 'tis there the birds oft love to dwell
And sip the honey from thy lips.

Annie Laurie

Edited by Max Spicker

Melody by LADY SCOTT
(Composed 1847)

Moderato assai
mf
mf
p
1. Max-welton braes are bon-nie, Where ear-ly fa's the_ dew, And it's
there that An-nie Lau-rie, Gie'd me her prom-ise true, Gie'd

cresc.
espress.
me her prom - ise true, Which ne'er for-got will be; And for
cresc.
p
poco riten.
p
bon - nie An - nie Lau - rie I'd lay me down and dee.
col canto
mf
mf
2. Her
brow is like the snaw drift, Her throat is like the swan, Her
dew on the gow - an ly - ing Is the fa' o' her fair - y feet, Like the
p

face, it is the fair-est, That e'er the sun shone on, That
winds in sum - mer sigh - ing, Her voice is low and sweet, Her
e'er the sun shone on; And dark blue is her e'e, And for
voice is low and sweet; She's a' the world to me, And for
cresc.
espress.
cresc
p
poco riten.
p
bon - nie An - nie_ Lau - rie I'd_ lay_ me down and dee.
bon - nie An - nie_ Lau - rie I'd_ lay_ me down and dee.
col canto
mf
2.
3.
p
3. Like

Auld Lang Syne

Robert Burns

Moderately
1. Should auld ac-quain-tance be for-got and nev-er brought to
2. We twa' ha'e ran a-boot the brae and pu'd the Gow-ans
mind? Should auld ac-quain-tance be for-got and days of Auld Lang Syne?
fine, We've wan-dered mony a wea-ry foot sin Auld_ Lang_ Syne?
For Auld_ Lang_ Syne, my dear, For Auld_ Lang_ Syne, We'll
tak' a cup o' kind-ness yet, For Auld_ Lang_ Syne.
D.C.
D.C.

Beautiful Isle of Somewhere

Lyrics by
Jessie Brown Pounds

Music by
John S. Fearis

Slowly
p
mp
1. Some-where the sun is shin - ing, Some-where the song-birds dwell,
2. Some-where the day is long - er, Some-where the task is done,
mp
poco rit.
Hush, then, thy sad re - pin - ing, God lives, and all is well.
Some-where the heart is strong - er, Some-where the guer - don won.
poco rit.

REFRAIN
mp a tempo
Some - where, some - where, Beau - ti - ful Isle_ of Some - where!
mp a tempo
mf
D. S.
Land of the true, where we live a - new, Beau - ti - ful Isle_of Some - where.
mf
D.S. for 2d verse
mp a tempo
rit.
mp a tempo
3. Some - where the load is lift - ed Close by an o - pen
mp a tempo

gate, Some-where the clouds are rift-ed,
poco rit.
Some-where the an-gels wait
REFRAIN
mp a tempo
Some-where, some-where,
Beau-ti-ful Isle of Some-where! Land of the true, where we
mf
live a-new, Beau-ti-ful Isle of Some-where.

Believe me, if all those endearing young charms

Thomas Moore

Air: "My lodging is on the cold ground."

Andantino

p
p
Be - lieve me, if all those en -
pp
dear - ing young charms which I gaze on so fond - ly to - day, Were to
change by to-mor-row, and fleet in my arms, Like fair-y gifts fad-ing a - way, Thou would'st
3

still be a-dor'd, as the mo-ment thou art, Let thy love-li-ness fade as it
mp
will, And a-round the dear ru-in each wish of my heart, Would en-
pp
twine it-self ver-dant-ly still. It
p
pp
p
is not while beau-ty and youth are thine own, And thy cheeks un-pro-fan'd by a tear, That the
pp

fer - vor and faith of a soul can be known, To which time will but make thee more
dear.___ No, the heart that has tru - ly loved nev - er for gets, But as
tru - ly loves on to the close,___ As the sun - flow-er turns on her god, when he sets, The same
look which she turn'd when he rose.___
p
rit.

A Bicycle Built for Two

Harry Dacre

Moderate Waltz Tempo

Dai - sy, Dai - sy, Give me your an - swer, do.
I'm half cra - zy, All for the love of you. It
won't be a sty - lish mar - riage; I can't af - ford a car - riage, But
you'll look sweet on a seat of a bi - cy - cle built for two.
f
p
f

The Blue Bells of Scotland

Moderately
1. Oh, where and oh, where is your_ high-land lad-die gone, Oh, where and oh, where is your_ high-land lad-die gone? He's gone to fight the foe for King George up-on the throne, And it's oh, in my heart, How I_ wish him safe at home.
2. Oh, where and oh, where does your_ high-land lad-die dwell, Oh, where and oh, where does your_ high-land lad-die dwell? He dwells in mer-ry Scot-land at the sign of the blue-bell, And it's oh, in my heart, How I_ love my lad-die well.
D.C.
D.C.

Brown October Ale

from "Robin Hood"

Reginald de Koven

Brightly
1. And it's will ye quaff with
2. And it's will ye love me
me, my lads, And it's will ye quaff with me? It is a draught of
true, my lads, And it's will ye love me true? If not, I'll drink one
nut-brown ale I offer unto ye. All humming in the
flagon more, And so farewell to you. If Jean or Moll, or
tankard, lads, It cheers the heart forlorn, Oh! here's a friend to
Nan or Doll Should make your heart to mourn, Fill up the pail with

più mosso
ev - 'ry-one, 'Tis stout John Bar - ley - corn.
nut-brown ale, And toast John Bar - ley - corn.
So laugh, lads, and quaff, lads, 'Twill
make you stout and hale, Through all my days I'll sing the praise Of brown Oc - to - ber
Chorus
Solo
ale. Yes, laugh, lads, and quaff, lads, 'Twill make you stout and hale, ah! Through
f
mf
Chorus
D.C.
all my days I'll sing the praise Of brown Oc-to - ber ale, Of brown Oc-to - ber ale.
D.C.

Calm as the Night

Still wie die Nacht

English version by
Nathan Haskell Dole

Carl Bohm

Poco tranquillo
Voice
Piano
p
rit.
p a tempo
Still wie die Nacht, tief wie das Meer,
Calm as the night, deep as the sea,
mf
soll dei - ne Lie - - be sein!
Should be thy love for me!
rit.
a tempo
p poco a poco cresc.
Still wie die Nacht und tief wie das Meer
Calm as the night, and deep as the sea,
f

soll dei - ne Lie - be, dei - ne Lie - be sein,
Should be thy love, should be thy love for me,
pp
poco rit.
soll dei - ne Lie - be sein!
should be thy love for me!
pp
poco rit.
pp a tempo
poco rit.
a tempo
mf
Wenn du mich liebst
If love like mine
mf
so wie ich dich, will ich dein ei - gen
glow in thy heart, I am for ev - er
p
rit.
p
rit.

a tempo
f con moto
sein. Heiss wie der Stahl, und
thine. Fer- vent as steel, and
a tempo
f con moto
ff
fest wie der Stein soll dei - ne Lie - be, dei - ne
firm as the hills, Should be thy love, should be thy
ff
p
rit.
Lie - be sein, soll dei - ne Lie - be
love for me, should be thy love for
p
rit.
a tempo
sein!
me!
rit.
p a tempo
pp

Carry me back to old Virginny

Song and Chorus

Words and Music by
James A. Bland

Moderato
Voice
Piano
mf
p
1. Car-ry me back to old Vir-gin-ny, There's where the cot-ton and the
2. Car-ry me back to old Vir-gin-ny, There let me live till I
corn and 'ta-toes grow, There's where the birds war-ble sweet in the spring-time,
with-er and de-cay, Long by the old dis-mal swamp have I wan-dered,

There's where the old dark-ey's heart am longed to go. There's where I la-bored so
There's where this old dark-ey's life will pass a-way. Mas - sa and mis-sis have
hard for old Mas-sa, Day af - ter day in the
long gone be-fore me, Soon we will meet on that
field of yel - low corn, No place on earth do I
bright and gold - en shore. There we'll be hap - py and
love more sin-cere-ly Than old Vir-gin-ny, the state where I was born.
free from all sor-row, There's where we'll meet and we'll nev - er part no more.
rit.
rit.

Refrain

SOPRANO
Car - ry me back to old Vir - gin - ny,
ALTO
Car - ry me back to old Vir - gin - ny,
TENOR
Car - ry me back to old Vir - gin - ny,
BASS
Car - ry me back to old Vir - gin - ny,
There's where the cot - ton and the corn and 'ta - toes grow.
There's where the cot - ton and the corn and 'ta - toes grow.
There's where the cot - ton and the corn and 'ta - toes grow.
There's where the cot - ton and the corn and 'ta - toes grow.

There's where the birds war - ble sweet in the spring-time,
There's where the birds war - ble sweet in the spring-time,
There's where the birds war - ble sweet in the spring-time,
There's where the birds war - ble sweet in the spring-time,
rit.
There's where this old dark - ey's heart am longed to go.
rit.
There's where this old dark - ey's heart am longed to go.
rit.
There's where this old dark - ey's heart am longed to go.
rit.
There's where this old dark - ey's heart am longed to go.
rit.

Repeat refrain pp after 2nd verse

Cielito Lindo

Dear Little Heaven

English version by
Lorraine Noel Finley

Folk Song
Arranged by Miguel Sandoval

Allegro
De - ba - jo
Un - der my
de mi ven - ta - na
win - dow a cow - boy
Pa - sa las no - ches ron -
Pass - es the night roam - ing

dan - do Un cha - rri - to muy va - lien - te
sad - ly; He's a lad of youth - ful vig - or,
Que me vie - ne e - na - mo - ran - do.
And he's come to love me mad - ly.
Ay, cha - rri - to, no me ron - des
But to an - oth - er I'm prom - ised;
Que de o - tro
If he should
soy pro - me - ti - da, Y si sa - be que me
learn of your woo - ing, O dear cow - boy, he might

rall.
bus - cas, Pue - de cos - tar - te la vi - da.
kill you! Love might then prove your un - do - ing.
rall. col canto
a tempo
Ay, cha - rro, por Dios, Ay, dé - ja - me en paz Y ol -
De - vo - tion must cease, So leave me in peace. For -
a tempo
rall.
più rall.
port.
vi - da mi a - mor Que no has de lo - grar.
get me, pray do; My love's not for you.
rall.
più rall.

a tempo
"E - se lu - nar que tie - nes, Cie - li - to
Si tu ma - má te di - ce, Cie - li - to
"You've a mark like a dim - ple, Dear lit - tle
Should your moth - er in - struct you, Dear lit - tle
a tempo
lin - do, Jun - to a la bo - ca,
lin - do, 'Cie - rra la puer - ta,'
Heav - en, Show - ing your plea - sure,
Heav - en, 'Bolt your door night - ly,'
No se lo des a na - die, Cie - li - to
Ha - ce rui - do a la lla - ve, Cie - li - to
Near your lips gai - ly smil - ing, Dear lit - tle
Though your rat - tle the han - dle, Dear lit - tle

lin - do, Que a mi me to - ca.
lin - do, Y de - ja - la a - bier - ta.
Heav - en, Guard it, my trea - sure.
Heav - en, Don't close it tight - ly.
¡Ay, ay, ay, ay! Can - ta y no
Ay, ay, ay, ay! Sing lest you're
llo - res Por - que can - tan - do se a - le - gran, Cie - li - to
tear - ful; In song let hap - pi - ness ech - o, Dear lit - tle
p
al Coda

1.
2.
Dal 𝄋 e poi al Coda
lin - do, Los co - ra - zo - nes.
zo - nes.
Heav - en, Sing and be cheer - ful!
cheer - ful!
Dal 𝄋 e poi al Coda
Coda
f
ten.
a tempo
lin - do, Los co - ra - zo - nes."
Heav - en, In song, be cheer - ful!"
f
a tempo
f

Comin' Through the Rye

Robert Burns

1. If a bod - y meet a bod - y, com - in' through the rye,
2. If a bod - y meet a bod - y, com - in' frae the town,
If a bod - y kiss a bod - y, need a bod - y cry?
If a bod - y greet a bod - y, need a bod - y frown?
Ev - 'ry las - sie has her lad - die, nane, they say, ha'e I, Yet
a' the lads they smile on me, When com - in' through the rye.
D. C.

Cradle-Song
Wiegenlied

Karl Simrock
English version by
Henry G. Chapman

Johannes Brahms
Op.49, No.4

Zart bewegt
Dolce, con moto
p
Gu-ten A-bend, gut' Nacht, mit
So good-night now once more, With
p
Ro-sen be-dacht, mit_ Näg-lein be-steckt, schlüpf' un-ter die
ros-es roof'd o'er,_ All_ tied up with bows, Slip_ un-der the
Deck': Mor-gen früh, wenn Gott will, wirst du wie-der ge-
clothes, When the morn-ing shall break, Please the Lord, thou wilt
weckt, mor-gen früh, wenn Gott will, wirst du wie-der ge-weckt!
wake, When the morn-ing shall break, Please the Lord, thou wilt wake!

p
Gu - ten A - bend, gut' Nacht, von -
Good - night then once more, By -
Eng - lein be - wacht, die - zei - gen im - Traum dir - Christ - kind - leins
an - gels watch'd o'er, - In - dreams thou shalt see A - fair Christ - mas -
Baum: Schlaf' nun se - lig und süss, schau' im Traum 's Pa - ra -
tree. Go to sleep, close thine eyes, Thou shalt see Par - a -
dies! schlaf' nun se - lig und süss, schau' im Traum 's Pa - ra - dies!
dise, Go to sleep, close thine eyes, Thou shalt see Par - a - dise!
p

Drink, Puppy, Drink

Hunting-Song

Moderato
Piano
f
rall.
mf
Here's to the fox in his earth be-low the rocks! And here's to the line that we fol-low, And
here's to the hound with his nose up-on the ground, Tho' mer-ri-ly we whoop and we hol-loa!
CHORUS
f
Then drink, pup-py, drink, and let ev-'ry pup-py drink, That is
f
f
cresc.

old e-nough to lap and to swal-low, For he'll grow in-to a hound, So we'll
fz
pass the bot - tle round, And mer - ri - ly we'll whoop and we'll hol - loa.
rall.
D. S.

2

Here's to the horse, and the rider too, of course;
And here's to the rally o' the hunt, boys;
Here's a health to every friend, who can struggle to the end,
And here's to the Tally-ho in front, boys. *Chorus*

3

Here's to the gap, and the timber that we rap,
Here's to the white thorn, and the black, too;
And here's to the pace that puts life into the chase,
And the fence that gives a moment to the pack, too. *Chorus*

4

Oh! the pack is staunch and true, now they run from scent to view,
And it's worth the risk to life and limb and neck, boys,
To see them drive and stoop till they finish with "Who-whoop",
Forty minutes on the grass without a check, boys. *Chorus*

"Drink to me only with thine eyes"

OLD ENGLISH AIR
Date uncertain

BEN JONSON
(1573 - 1637)

Very smoothly, and rather slow
Voice
Piano
p
cresc.
p
pp
Drink to me on - ly with thine eyes, And I — will pledge with mine, —
Or leave a kiss with - in — the cup, — And I'll — not ask for wine; — The

thirst_ that from the soul_ doth rise, Doth ask a drink di - vine,__
But might I of Jove's nec - tar sip,_ I would not change for
pp
cresc.
thine!
mf
cresc.
I sent thee late a ros - y wreath, Not so_ much hon'ring thee ___
pp

As giv - ing it a hope that there_ It could not with - er'd
be;_ But thou_ there - on didst on - ly breathe And
sent'st it back to me;_ Since when it grows, and
smells, I swear, Not of_ it - self, but thee!
pp
cresc.
mf

For He's a Jolly Good Fellow

Brightly
1. For he's a jol - ly good fel - low, For he's a jol - ly good fel - low, For he's a jol - ly good fel - low, Which no - bod - y can de - ny, Which no - bo - dy can de - ny.
2. We won't go home un - til morn - ing, We won't go home un - til morn - ing, We won't go home un - til morn - ing, Till day - light does ap - pear, Till day - light does ap - pear.
3. The bear went o - ver the moun - tain, The bear went o - ver the moun - tain, The bear went o - ver the moun - tain, To see what he could see, To see what he could see.
4. The oth - er side of the moun - tain, The oth - er side of the moun - tain, The oth - er side of the moun - tain, Was all that he could see.
Fine
D. C.

Good Night, Ladies

Moderately
1. Good - night, la - dies,_ Good - night, la - dies!_
2. Fare - well, la - dies,_ Fare - well, la - dies!_
3. Sweet dreams, la - dies,_ Sweet dreams la - dies!_
Good - night la - dies,_ We're going to leave you now.
Fare - well la - dies,_ We're going to leave you now.
Sweet dreams la - dies,_ We're going to leave you now.
Mer - ri - ly we roll a - long, Roll a - long, roll a - long,
Mer - ri - ly we roll a - long, O'er the deep blue sea.

Greensleeves

Words Traditional

Old English Folk-Tune
Arranged by William Stickles

Moderato
Voice
Piano
mp
mf
1. A -
lias, my love, you do me wrong, To cast me off — dis - cour - teous - ly, And
2. I've been read - y at your hand, To grant what - ev - er you would crave; And
mp
I have loved you, oh, so long, De - light - ing in — your com - pa - ny.
I have waged both life and land Your love and good will — for to have.

mf
Green - sleeves was all my joy, Green - sleeves was my de-light.
mf
Green-sleeves was my heart of gold, and who but my la - dy Green-sleeves.
mf
1.
2.
mp
3. Thou
couldst de-sire no earth-ly thing, But still thou hadst it read-i-ly; Thy
I will pray to God on high That thou my con-stan-cy may-est see; For
mp

mu - sic still — to play and sing, - And yet — thou wouldst — not love me.
I am still — thy lov - er true, - Come once - a - gain — and love me.
mf
Green - sleeves was all my joy, — Green - sleeves was my de - light,
mf
Green - sleeves was my heart of gold - And who but my la - dy Green - sleeves.
mf
1.
mp
2.
4. Well,

Gypsy Love Song

Words by
Harry B. Smith

Music by
Victor Herbert

Molto tranquillo
VOICE
PIANO
The birds of the for-est are call-ing for thee,_ And the shades and the glades are lone-ly;___ Sum-mer is there with her blos-soms fair,_____ And you___ are ab - sent on-ly.___ No
The fawn that you tamed has a look in its eyes,_That doth say: "We are too___ long part-ed;"___ Songs that are trolled by our com-rades old,_____ Are not now, as they were,__ light heart-ed.___ The

bird___ that nests in the green-wood tree,___ But sighs___ to greet you and
wild rose fades in the leaf - y shades, Its ghost___ will find you and
kiss you, All the vi - o - lets yearn, yearn for your safe re - turn, But
haunt you, All the friends say: "Come, come to your wood - land home," And
ten.
frit.
most of all___ I miss you.___
most of all___ I want you.___
ten.
frit.
ten.
REFRAIN
Andante
p a tempo
Slum - ber cn, my lit - tle gyp - sy sweet - heart, Dream of the field and the
dolcissimo
p
a tempo

p
grove, Can you hear me, hear me in that dream-land,
Where your fan - cies rove?
mp
Slum - ber on, my
lit - tle gyp - sy sweet-heart, Wild lit - tle wood - land dove,
rit.
p a tempo
Can you hear the song that tells you All my heart's true love?
molto rit.

Here's to the Maiden

Words by
Richard Brinsley Sheridan (1776)

Allegretto moderato
1 Here's to the maid - en of bash - ful fif - teen,
2 Here's to the char - mer whose dim - ples we prize,
3 Here's to the maid with a bo - som of snow, Now to
4 For let her be clum - sy or let her be slim, Young or
Piano
Now to the wid - ow of fif - ty; Here's to the flaunt - ing, ex -
Now to the dam - sel with none, sir; Here's to the girl with a
her that's as brown as a ber - ry; Here's to the wife with a
an - cient, I care not a fea - ther; So fill up a bum - per, nay,
tra - va - gant queen, And here's to the house-wife that's thrif - ty. Let the toast pass,
pair of blue eyes, And now to the nymph with but one, sir. Let the toast pass,
face full of woe, And here's to the dam - sel that's mer - ry. Let the toast pass,
fill to the brim, And e'en let us toast 'em to - geth - er. Let the toast pass,

drink to the lass; I war - rant she'll prove an ex - cuse for the glass.
drink to the lass; I war - rant she'll prove an ex - cuse for the glass.
drink to the lass; I war - rant she'll prove an ex - cuse for the glass.
drink to the lass; I war - rant she'll prove an ex - cuse for the glass.
CHORUS
f
Let the toast pass, drink to the lass; I
Let the toast pass, drink to the
f
war - rant she'll prove an ex - cuse for the glass.
lass; she'll prove an ex - cuse for the glass.

Home on the Range

Arranged by
Jeffrey Marlowe

Andante moderato
p
1. Oh, give me a home where the buf - fa - lo roam, Where the deer and the an - te - lope play; Where sel - dom is heard a dis -
2. Oh, give me a land where the bright dia - mond sand Flows lei - sure - ly down the stream; Where the grace - ful, white swan goes
3. Where the air is so pure, the zeph - yrs so free, And the breez - es balm - y and light, That I would not ex - change my
4. How of - ten at night, when the heav - ens are bright With the light of the glit - ter - ing stars, Have I stood there a - mazed and
mf
rit.
p a tempo

cour - ag - ing word, And the skies are not cloud - y all day.
glid - ing a - long Like a maid in a heav - en - ly dream.
home on the range For all of the cit - ies so bright.
asked, as I gazed, If their glo - ry ex - ceeds that of ours.
mf CHORUS
Home, home on the range Where the deer and the an - te-lope
mf
play; Where sel - dom is heard a dis - cour - ag - ing word, And the
skies are not cloud - y all day.
1.
2.
day.
rit.

Home, Sweet Home

John Howard Payne

Sir Henry R. Bishop

Moderato
Voice
Piano
p
cresc.
dim.
pp
'Mid pleas - ures and
pal - aces though we may roam,
Be it ev - er so

hum - ble, there's no place like home. A charm from the
f
skies seems to hal - low us there, Which, seek through the
world, is ne'er met with else-where. Home, home,
dolce.
pp
ad lib.
sweet, sweet home; There's no place like home! There's no place like
pp

home! An
exile from home, splendor dazzles in vain, Oh!
pp
give me my lowly thatch'd cottage again; The
As sung by Jenny Lind.
birds sing - ing gai - ly, that
birds sing - ing gai - ly, that came at my call, Give me
cresc.

them, with the peace of mind, dear - er than all!
dim.
f
dim.
pp
Home, home, sweet, sweet home! There's
f
tr
pp
no place like home, there is no place like home!
pp

"I love thee"
„Ich liebe dich"

German words translated from the Danish by
F. von Holstein
English version by
Henry G. Chapman

Edvard Grieg

Andante
Voice
Piano
p
Du mein Ge -
Thou art my
p
dan - ke, du mein Sein und Wer - den!
thoughts, my pres - ent and my fu - ture,
pp
Du mei - nes
Thou art my
pp
f
Her - zens er - ste Se - lig - keit!
heart's su - preme, its on - ly joy;
Ped.
*
Ped.
*

p
Ich lie - be dich wie nichts auf die - ser Er - den, ich lie - be dich, ich
I love thee more than an - y earth - ly crea - ture, I love thee, dear, I
Ped.
cresc. sempre
ff
lie - be dich, ich lie - be dich in Zeit und E - wig - keit! Ich
love thee, dear, I love thee now and for e - ter - ni - ty! I
cresc. sempre
Ped.
ritard.
lie - be dich in Zeit und E - wig - keit!
love thee now and for e - ter - ni - ty!
ff
ritard.
mp
dim.
Ped.
Ped.
p
pp
Ich den - ke dein, kann stets nur dei - ner den - ken, nur dei - nem
One thought of thee all oth - er thought drives from me, Pledged to thy
a tempo
pp
Ped.

Glück ist dies-ses Herz ge-weiht; wie Gott auch
good a-lone this heart shall be; For to what-
mag des Le-bens Schick-sal len-ken, ich lie-be dich, ich
ev-er fate God's will may doom me, I love thee, dear, I
cresc. sempre
lie-be dich, ich lie-be dich in Zeit und E-wig-keit! Ich
love thee, dear, I love thee now and for e-ter-ni-ty, I
cresc. sempre
ritard.
lie-be dich in Zeit und E-wig-keit!
love thee now and for e-ter-ni-ty!
ritard.
dim.

I Love You Truly

Words and Music by
CARRIE JACOBS-BOND

Andante con amore
p
I love you tru - ly, tru - ly,
p legato
p sempre legato
dear, Life with its sor - row, life with its tear, Fades in - to
dreams when I feel you are near, For I love you tru-ly, tru - ly, dear.
rall.
rall.

p
Ah! love, 'tis some-thing to feel your kind
p legato
p sempre legato
hand, Ah! yes, 'tis some-thing by your side to stand; Gone is the
sor - row, Gone doubt and fear, For you love me tru-ly, tru-ly, dear.
rall.
rall.

517

I've Been Workin' On the Railroad

Moderately
I've been work-in' on the rail - road, All the live long day.
I've been work-in' on the rail - road, Just to pass the time a - way.
Don't you hear the whis-tle blow - in'? Rise up so ear - ly in the morn,
Don't you hear the cap-tain shout - ing: "Din - ah, blow your horn."

John Peel

Arr. by John Tait

With spirit
Piano
1. D'ye ken John Peel with his coat so gay, D'ye ken John Peel at the
2. Yes, I ken John Peel and Ru - by too! Ran - ter and Ring - wood,
3. Then here's to John Peel from my heart and soul, Let's drink to his health, let's
4. D'ye ken John Peel with his coat so gay? He liv'd at Trout - beck
break of the day, D'ye ken John Peel when he's
Bell - man and True, From a find to a check, from a
fin - ish the bowl. We'll fol - low John Peel thro'
once on a day; Now he has gone far,
far, far a - way, With his hounds and his horn in the morn - ing?
check to a view, From a view to a death in the morn - ing.
fair and thro' foul, If we want a good hunt in the morn - ing.
far, far, a - way; We shall ne'er hear his voice in the morn - ing.

CHORUS
For the sound of his horn brought me from my bed, And the
cry of his hounds which he oft - times led;
Peel's view hal - loo would a -
wak - en the dead, Or the fox from his lair in the morn - ing.
D. C.
D. C.

Juanita

Spanish Ballad

Words by the
Hon. Mrs. Norton

Allegretto
Voice
Piano
p
1. Soft o'er the foun - tain, Ling'ring falls the south-ern moon:
2. When in thy dream - ing Moons like these shall shine a - gain,
Far o'er the moun - tain Breaks the day too soon!
And day - light beam - ing Prove thy dreams are vain,
In thy dark eyes' splen - dour, Where the warm light loves to dwell,
Wilt thou not, re - lent - ing, For thine ab - sent lov - er sigh,

Meno mosso
Wear - y looks, yet ten - der Speak their fond fare - well!
In thy heart con - sent - ing To a prayer gone by?
a tempo
p
Ni - ta! Jua - ni - ta! Ask thy soul if we should part!
Ni - ta! Jua - ni - ta! Let me lin - ger by thy side!
mf
rall.
Ni - ta! Jua - ni - ta! Lean thou on my heart!
Ni - ta! Jua - ni - ta! Be my own fair bride!

Just A-Wearyin' For You

Words by
FRANK STANTON

Music by
CARRIE JACOBS-BOND

Moderato
1. Just a-wear-y-in' for you, All the time a-feel-in' blue,
3. Eve-nin' comes, I miss you more When the dark gloom's round the door,
Wish-in' for you, wond'-rin' when You'll be com-in' home a-gain. Rest-less, don't know
Seems just like you or-ter be There to o-pen it for me. Latch goes tink-lin',
what to do, Just a-wear-y-in' for you.
thrills me through, Sets me wear-y-in' for you.
mf
p
cresc.
f
rall.
Fine

p
2. Morn - - in' comes, the birds a - wake,
12
8
delicato
Used to sing so for your sake
mf
But there's sad-ness
in the notes That come trill - in' from their throats.
p
cresc.
Seem to feel your
ab-sence, too, Just a-wear-y - in' for you.
f
rall.
D. S. al Fine

The Last Rose of Summer

Qui sola vergin rosa

Thomas Moore

Old Irish Air*
Piano accompaniment by Carl Deis

Slow
Voice
Piano
mp
1.'Tis the last rose of summer, Left blooming a - lone. All her
1. Qui so - la ver - gin ro - sa, Co - me puoi tu fio - rir? An -
2. I'll not leave thee, thou lone one, To pine on the stem; Since the
love - ly companions Are fa - ded and gone. No
co - ra mez - zo a - sco - sa E pres - so gia a mo - rir! Non
love - ly are sleep - ing, Go sleep thou with them. Thus
più f

*Used by Friedrich von Flotow in his famous opera "Martha"

poco rit.
a tempo
p
flow - er of her kin - dred, No rose - bud is nigh, To re-
ha per te ru-gia - de, Gia col - ta sei dal gel! Il
kind - ly I'll scat - ter Thy leaves on the bed, Where thy
flect back her blush - es, Or give sigh for
ca - po tuo già ca - de, Chi - no sul ver - de
mates of the gar - den Lie scent - less and
sigh!
stel.
dead.
mf
cresc.
dim. e rit.

mp
3. So soon may I fol-low When friend-ships de-cay, And from
2. Per-chè so-la i-gno-ra-ta Lan-guir nel tuo giar-din, Dal
a tempo
mp sempre arpeggiando
love's shin-ing cir-cle The gems drop a-way. When
ven-to tor-men-ta-ta In pre-da a un rio des-tin? Sul
true hearts lie with-ered, And fond ones are flown, Oh!
ce-spi-te tre-man-te Ti col-go, gio-vin fior! Su
colla voce
who would in-hab-it This bleak world a-lone?
que-sto co-re a-man-te Co-si mor-rai d'a-mor.

Listen To the Mocking Bird

Alice Hawthorne

Moderately
1. I'm dream - ing now of Hal - lie, Sweet Hal - lie, Sweet
2. Ah, well I yet re - mem - ber, re - mem - ber, re -
Hal - lie, I'm dream - ing now of Hal - lie, For the
mem - ber, Ah, well I yet re - mem - ber When we
thought of her is one that nev - er dies. She's sleep - ing in the
gath - ered in the cot - ton side by side. 'Twas in the mild Sep -
val - ley, the val - ley, the val - ley, She's sleep - ing in the
tem - ber, Sep - tem - ber, Sep - tem - ber, 'Twas in the mild Sep -

val - ley, And the mock-ing bird is sing-ing where she lies.
tem - ber, And the mock-ing bird was sing-ing far and wide.
Chorus
Lis-ten to the mock-ing bird, Lis-ten to the mock-ing bird, The
mock-ing bird still sing-ing o'er her grave, Lis-ten to the mock-ing bird, Lis-ten to the
mock-ing bird, Still sing-ing where the weep-ing wil - lows wave.
D.C.
D.C.

The Little Brown Jug

Allegretto
Voice
Piano
mf
p
1. My wife and I liv'd all a-lone In a lit-tle log-hut we call'd our own;
She lov'd gin, and I lov'd rum, I tell you what, we'd lots of fun.
2. 'Tis you who make my friends my foes, 'Tis you who make me wear old clothes;
Here you are, so near my nose, So tip her up and down she goes.

CHORUS
Ha, ha, ha, you and me, "Lit - tle brown jug, don't I love thee,

D. C.
Ha, ha, ha, you and me, "Lit - tle brown jug," don't I love thee.
D. C.

3.

When I go toiling to my farm,
  I take little "Brown Jug" under my arm;
I place it under a shady tree,
  Little "Brown Jug," 'tis **you** and me. *Chorus.*

4.

If all the folks in Adam's race
  Were gather'd together in one place;
Then I'd prepare to shed a tear,
  Before I'd part from you, my dear. *Chorus.*

5.

If I'd a cow that gave such milk,
  I'd clothe her in the finest silk;
I'd feed her on the choicest hay,
  And milk her forty times a day. *Chorus.*

6.

The rose is red, my nose is, too,
  The violet's blue, and so are you;
And yet I guess before I stop,
  We'd better take another drop. *Chorus.*

Long, Long Ago

THOMAS HAYNES BAYLY
(1797-1839)

Moderato
PIANO
mf
mf
1. Tell me the tales that to me were so dear, Long, long a - go,
2. Do you re - mem - ber the path where we met, Long, long a - go,
3. Though by your kind - ness my fond hopes were raised, Long, long a - go,
mf
long, long a - go, Sing me the songs I de - light - ed to hear,
long, long a - go, Ah, yes! you told me you ne'er would for - get,
long, long a - go, You by more el - o - quent lips have been praised,

Long, long a - go, long a - go. Now you are come all my
Long, long a - go, long a - go. Then to all oth - ers my
Long, long a - go, long a - go. But by long ab - sence your
grief is re - moved, Let me for - get that so long you have roved,
smile you pre - fer'd, Love when you spoke gave a charm to each word,
truth has been tried, Still to your ac - cents I lis - ten with pride,
rit.
Let me be - lieve that you love as you loved, Long long a - go, long a -
Still my heart treas - ures the prais - es I heard, Long long a - go, long a -
Blest as I was when I sat by your side, Long long a - go, long a -
rit.
go.
go.
go.
a tempo

The Lost Chord

Adelaide A. Procter

Arthur Sullivan

Andante moderato
Piano
p
cresc.
f
dim.
p
p
Seat-ed one day at the
or-gan, I was wear-y and ill at ease, And my fin-gers wan-der'd i-dly
O-ver the nois-y keys; I know not what I was play-ing, Or
cresc.
cresc.

what I was dream-ing then, But I struck one chord of mu-sic Like the
dim.
p
sound of a great A-men, like the sound of a great A-
cresc.
f
poco rall.
dim.
men. It
p cresc.
f
dim.
Ped.
flood-ed the crim-son twi-light Like the close of an an-gel's Psalm, And it
cresc.
p

dim.
lay on my fe-ver'd spir - it With a touch of in-fin-ite calm; It
dim.
cresc.
dim.
qui-et-ed pain and sor-row Like love o-ver-com-ing strife, It
cresc.
dim.
seem'd the har-mo-nious e - cho From our dis-cord-ant life. It
p
p tranquillo
tranquillo sempre
link'd all per-plex-ed mean-ings, In-to one per - fect peace, And

poco a poco più animato
f agitato
trem-bled a-way in-to si-lence, As if it were loth to cease. I have
cresc. animando
f agitato
Ped. *
sought, but I seek it vain-ly, That one lost chord di-vine, Which
f
came from the soul of the or-gan, And en-ter'd in-to
Grandioso
f
mine. It may be, that Death's bright an-gel Will
cresc. molto. ritard. f ff

speak in that chord a-gain; It may be, that on-ly in Heav'n I shall
sempre ff
hear that grand A-men. It may be, that Death's bright an-gel Will
sf
sf
ff
ritard.
con gran
speak in that chord a-gain, It may be, that on-ly in Heav'n I shall
fff
ritard.
colla voce
con gran
forza
hear that grand A-men.
forza
a tempo
rall.

Love's Old, Sweet Song

Words by
G. Clifton Bingham

J. L. Molloy

Andante con moto
rit.
a tempo.
Ped.
Once in the dear dead days beyond re-call, When on the world the mists be-gan to fall,
Out of the dreams that rose in hap-py throng Low to our hearts Love sung an old sweet song;

And in the dusk where fell the fire-light gleam, Soft-ly it wove it-self in - to our dream.
rit.
p a tempo
Just a song at twi-light, when the lights are low, And the flick-'ring shadows
p
soft-ly come and go, Tho' the heart be wea - ry, sad the day and long,
f
mf
Still to us at twi - light comes Love's old song, comes Love's old sweet — song.
rit.
f rit.
sempre Ped.

mf
E-ven to-day we hear Love's song of yore, Deep in our hearts it dwells for e-ver-more
p
Foot-steps may fal-ter, weary grow the way, Still we can hear it at the close of day.
mf
So till the end, when life's dim shadows fall, Love will be found the sweetest song of all.
p

a tempo.
Just a song at twi-light, when the lights are low, And the flick-'ring
p cantando.
sempre Ped. Ped.
shad-ows soft-ly come and go; Tho' the heart be wea-ry
f
mf
Ped. Ped.
sad the day and long, Still to us at twi - light comes Love's old song, comes
ad lib.
Love's old sweet song.
f animato.
rit.
Ped. Ped.

My Bonnie

Scotch Song

Moderately
1. My Bon - nie lies o - ver the o - cean,
2. Last night as I lay on my pil - low,
3. O blow, ye winds, o - ver the o - cean,
My Bon - nie lies o - ver the sea,
Last night as I lay on my bed,
O blow, ye winds, o - ver the sea,
My Bon - nie lies o - ver the o - cean,
Last night as I lay on my pil - low,
O blow, ye winds, o - ver the o - cean,

Oh, bring back my Bon - nie to me.
I dreamt that my Bon - nie was dead.
And bring back my Bon - nie to me.
Bring back, bring back, bring back my
Bon - nie to me, to me; Bring back, bring
back, Oh, bring back my Bon - nie to me.
D.C.
D.C.

My Wild Irish Rose

Words and Music by
Chauncey Olcott

Moderately
Piano
mf
rit.
p a tempo
If you lis - ten, I'll sing you a sweet lit - tle song Of a flow - er that's now drooped and dead, Yet dear - er to me, Yes, than all of its mates, Tho' each holds a - loft its proud head. 'Twas
They may sing of their ro - ses which by oth - er names, Would smell just as sweet - ly, they say, But I know that my Rose would nev - er con - sent To have that sweet name tak - en a - way. Her
p
mf

giv - en to me by a girl that I know; Since we've met, faith, I've
glanc - es are shy when - e'er I pass by The bow - er where
p
known no re - pose, She is dear - er by far than the
my true love grows. And my one wish has been that some
p
rit.
world's bright - est star, And I call her my wild I - rish rose.
day I may win The heart of my wild I - rish rose.
rit.
REFRAIN (with much expression)
mf a tempo
My wild I - rish rose, The sweet - est flow'r that grows,
mf
a tempo

You may search ev - 'ry - where, but none can com - pare With my
wild I - rish rose. My wild I - rish rose,
The dear - est flow'r that grows, And some day for my
sake, she may let me take The bloom from my wild I - rish rose.
mf
mf
rit.
rit.

None but the lonely heart

Nur wer die Sehnsucht kennt

English version by Arthur Westbrook
after the German of Johann Wolfgang von Goethe

Peter Ilyitch Tchaikovsky, Op. 6, No. 6

Andante non tanto
Piano
p espress.
p
Voice
p espress.
None but the lone - ly heart Can know my sad - ness,
Nur wer die Sehn - sucht kennt, weiss, was ich lei - de!
A - lone and part - ed far From joy and glad - ness.
Al - lein und ab - ge - trennt von al - ler Freu - de,
più f

Seh' ich an's
'Tis on - ly
un poco marcato
p
Fir - ma - ment nach je - ner Sei - te. Ach! der mich
yon I see The skies a - bove me; Ah! far a -
mf
liebt und kennt, ist in der Wei - te. Nur, wer die
way is he Who knows and loves me! One who has
pp
f
cresc.
Sehn - sucht kennt, weiss, was ich lei - de! Al - lein und
yearn'd, a - lone Can know my an - guish! Where ev - 'ry
p
cresc.

cresc. e string.
f
ab-ge-trennt von al - - ler Freu - de, al-lein ___ und ab-ge -
joy is flown For-lorn I lan - guish, Where ev - - 'ry joy is
cresc. e string.
ff
pp molto riten.
trennt ___ von al-ler Freu - de! Es schwindelt
flown ___ For-lorn I lan - guish! With heart on
ff
a tempo
mir, ___ es brennt mein Ein - - ge-wei - de, nur, wer die
fire ___ I swoon In end - - less an - - guish! One who has
espress.
Sehn - sucht kennt, weiss, was ich lei - de!
yearn'd, a - lone Knows how I lan-guish!
pp

'O sole mio!
My Sunshine

Poem by G. Capurro
English version by
Henry G. Chapman

E. di Capua

Andantino
Piano
mf
Voice
p
p
Che bel - la co - sa
Oh! what's so fine, dear,
'na iur - na - ta 'e so - le, n'a - ria se - re - na dop - - po 'na tem -
As a day of sun - shine? The sky is clear at last, The rain and
pe - - sta! Pe' ll'a - ria fre - sca pa - re già 'na fe - sta-
storm are past, Thro' air so cool, so bright, Comes the fes - tal sun - light.

cresc.
Che bel-la co-sa 'na iur-na-ta'e so-le. Ma n'a-tu
Oh! what's so fine, dear, As a day of sun-shine? An-oth-er
mf
so-le cchiù bel-lo,ohi-nè, 'o so-le mi-o sta 'nfron-te a
sun-light Far love-lier lies, Oh my own sun-shine! In your dear
te, 'o so-le,'o so-le mi-o
eyes! Oh sun-shine, my own sun-shine,
f
p
sta 'nfron-te a te, sta 'nfron-te a te!
In your dear eyes, in your dear eyes!

Oh, My Darling Clementine

P. Montrose

Moderately
In a cav-ern, in a can-yon, Ex-ca-vat-ing for a mine, Dwelt a min-er for-ty-nin-er, And his daugh-ter Cle-men-tine.
Light she was and like a fair-y, And her shoes were num-ber nine, Her-ring box-es with-out top-ses, San-dals were for Cle-men-tine.
Drove she duck-lings to the wa-ter Ev-'ry morn-ing just at nine, Hit her foot a-gainst a splin-ter, Fell in-to the foam-ing brine.
Ru-by lips a-bove the wa-ter Blow-ing bub-bles soft and fine, But, a-las, I was no swim-mer, So I lost my Cle-men-tine.
Oh, my dar-ling, oh, my dar-ling, oh, my dar-ling Cle-men-tine, You are lost and gone for-ev-er, Dread-ful sor-ry, Cle-men-tine.
D.C.
D.C.

Oh Promise Me

Clement Scott

R. DeKoven, Op. 50

Moderato
Voice
Piano
p
pesante
f
mf
Oh prom-ise me, that some day you and I Will
take our love to-geth-er to some sky Where

semplice
p
poco rall.
we can be a-lone, and faith re-new, And find the hol-lows where those flow-ers
cresc.
p poco rall.
a tempo
p con tenerezza
grew, Those first sweet vi-o-lets of ear-ly spring, Which
p marc. la melodia
cresc.
come in whis-pers, thrill us both, and sing Of love un-speak-a-ble that
cresc.
f rall.
is to be; Oh prom-ise me! oh prom-ise me!
f rall.

poco rubato
mf
a tempo
p
Oh
pesante
f
p
prom-ise me, that you will take my hand, The most un-wor-thy in this lone-ly
land, And let me sit be-side you, in your eyes
cresc.
ff largamente e con passione
See-ing the vi-sion of our par-a-dise, Hear-ing God's mes-sage while the
cresc.
colla voce
ff
Ped.

or - gan rolls Its might - y mu-sic to our
ver - y souls; No love less per-fect than a life with thee; Oh
prom-ise me! Oh prom - ise me!
con forza
rall.
ff
a tempo
dim.
p
rall.
pp
Ped.

On Wings of Song

H. Heine
English version by
Henry G. Chapman

F. MENDELSSOHN
Edited by Max Spicker

Andante tranquillo
p
1. Auf Flü - geln des — Ge - san - ges, Herz -
1. I'll bear thee off, — my dear - est, Up -
(2.) Veil - chen ki-chern und ko - sen, und
(2.) vio - lets whis-per to-geth - er, And
Andante tranquillo
Piano
pp
sempre p e legato
lieb - chen, trag' ich dich fort, fort nach den Flu - ren des
on the wings of my song, Off to a spot that I
schau'n nach den Ster-nen em - por; heim - lich er - zäh-len die
peek at the stars from their dell, And there to each oth - er the
Gan - ges, dort weiss ich den schön - sten — Ort. Dort
know of, Where Gan - ges rolls a - long. For
Ro - sen sich duf - ten - de Mähr - chen in's Ohr. Es
ros - es Their sweet-scent-ed fair - y tales — tell. The
sf
p

liegt ein roth-blü-hen-der Gar - - ten im stil - len Mon - den -
there in a beau-ti-ful gar - - den, While Cyn - thia rides — in
hüp-fen her-bei — und lau - - schen die from - men, klu-gen Ga -
dain-ty ga-zelles — will lis - - ten, And cau - tious-ly — ex -
cre - - - scen - - do
schein, — die Lo - tos-blu-men er-war - - ten ihr
state, — The lo - tus-blos-soms for thee, dear, Their
zell'n; — und in der Fer - ne rau - schen des
plore, — While aye is heard in the dis - tance The
dim.
p
trau - tes Schwe - ster - lein, — die Lo - tos-blu-men er -
dar - ling sis - ter, wait. — The lo - tus-blos-soms for
heil' - gen Stro - mes Well'n, — und in der Fer - ne
sa - cred riv - er's roar, — While aye is heard in the
di - mi - nu - en - do pp

cresc.
p
war - - - - - - - - ten ihr trau - tes Schwe - ster -
thee, dear, Their dar - ling sis - ter,
cresc.
p
rau - - - - - - - - schen des heil' - gen Stro - mes
dis - - - - - - - - tance The sa - cred riv - er's
p
lein.
wait.
Well'n.
roar.
cresc.
sf
dim.
1.
p
2. Die
2. There
2.
3. Dort wol - len wir nie - der -
3. And there we shall lie to -
p
cresc.
Ped.
*

sin - ken un - ter dem Pal - men - baum, und Lieb' und Ru - he
geth - er, There by the palm - y streams, In love and peace for
cresc.
Ped.
cresc.
sf
trin - ken und träu - men se - li - gen Traum, und
ev - er, And dream our hap - py dreams, and
cresc.
f
cresc.
dim.
träu - men se - li - gen Traum,
dream our hap - py dreams, our
dim.
p
Ped.
sel' - gen Traum.
hap - py dreams.
pp
Ped.

La Paloma
The Dove

English version by
Henry G. Chapman

S. Yradier

Allegretto
Piano
Voice
1. The day that I left Ha - ba - na, (The Lord be praised!)
2. But now we shall soon be mar - ried, (The Lord be praised!)
1. Cuan - do sa - li de la Ha - ba - na, ¡Val - ga - me Dios!
2. El dia que nos ca - se - mos, ¡Val - ga - me Dios!

Not one came to see me off, Ex-cept my-self,
One week it will soon be gone, I laugh for joy.
Na-die me ha vis-to sa-lir, Si-no fui yo,
En la se-ma-na que hay ir me ha-ce re-ir.
And one pret-ty Mex-i-ca-na: But what cared we?
And when at the church we've tar-ried, The knot to tie,
Yu-na lin-da Gau-chi-nan-ga A-llà voy yo,
Des-de la y-gle-sia jun-ti-tos, Que si se-ñor,
Who came, well in fact just came A-long with me.
We'll look for a place to sleep (And what care I!)
Que se vi-no tras de mi, Que si se-ñor.
Nos i-re-mos a dor-mir, A-llá voy yo.

1-2. If to thy win - dow ev - er shall come a wee dove,
1-2. Siá tu ven - ta - na lle - ga u - na Pa - lo - ma,
Treat it with kind - ness, for thou wilt find 'tis me, love,
Tra - ta - la con ca - ri - ño, que es mi per - so - na,
Tell it thy love, ah! tell it thy love for me, dear!
Cuen - ta - la tus a - mo - res, bien de mi vi - da,
Crown it with flow'rs, be-cause it has come to thee, dear. Do, my dar-ling, I pray!
Co - ro - na - la de flo - res, que es co - sa mi - a. ¡Ay! chi - ni - ta que si,

Thou must give me thy love, ah! So come with me, come with me, dar - ling,
¡ay! que da - me tu a - mor, ¡ay! Que ven - te con - mi - go chi - ni - ta
come with me where I dwell! Do, my dar - ling, I pray! Thou must give me thy
a - dón - de vi - vo yo. ¡Ay! chi - ni - ta que si, ¡ay! que da - me tu a -
love, ah! So come with me, come with me, dar - ling, come with me where I
mor, ¡ay! Que ven - te con - mi - go chi - ni - ta a - dón - de vi - vo
1. dwell! yo.
2. dwell! yo.

Plaisir d'amour
Joy of Love

Piano accompaniment
revised by Carl Deis

Giovanni Martini
(1741 - 1816)

With deep feeling
Piano
p
Voice
mf
The
Plai-
sf
joy of love comes on - ly to de - part; Its
sir d'a - mour ne du - re qu'un mo - ment, Cha-
mp
cresc.
cresc.
sor - rows bit - ter through a life - time prove. I
grin d'a - mour du - re tou - te la vi - e. J'ai
f
mf
mf

sfz
gave up all for cru - el Syl - via's love;
tout quit - té pour l'in-gra-te Sil-vi - - e,
sfz
rit.
p
Too soon I find an-oth-er owns her heart. The
El - le me quit-te et prend un au - tre a - mant. Plai-
f
rit.
a tempo
joy of love comes on-ly to de-part; Its
sir d'a - mour ne du - re qu'un mo - ment, Cha-
a tempo
p
sor - rows bit - ter through a life - time prove.
grin d'a - mour du-re tou-te la vi - e.
mf

p
"Long as the stream - let its waves may soft - ly pour, The
Tant que cet-te eau cou - le-ra dou - ce-ment Vers
cresc.
mead - ow pass - ing on its joy - ous way,
ce ruis-seau qui bor - de la prai - ri - e,
mp
My love shall be thine," would Syl - via soft - ly say.
Je t'ai - me - rai, me ré - pé - tait Sil - vi - e.
mp
rit.
Still flows the stream, but Syl - via loves no more.
L'eau cou - le en - cor, el - le a chan - gé pour - tant.

p a tempo
The joy of love comes on - ly to de -
Plai - sir d'a - mour ne du - re qu'un mo -
a tempo
p
cresc.
part; Its sor - rows bit - ter through a
ment, Cha - grin d'a - mour du - re tou - te la
cresc.
life - time prove.
vi - - - e.
p
mf
pp
mf
rit.

The Rosary

Le Rosaire

Der Rosenkranz

ROBERT CAMERON ROGERS
French version by Mme. C. Eschig
German version by Carl Engel

ETHELBERT NEVIN

Lento ed intimo
VOICE
PIANO
The hours I spent with thee, dear heart
Comme un ro - sai - re sont pour moi
Oft denk' mit Weh - mut ich zu - rück
Are as a string of pearls to me;
Les heu-res qui nous u - nis - saient,
Der hol-den Stun-den, reich an Glück,
I count them o-ver ev-'ry
Tou-jours je les comp-te pen -
Die, strah-lend in der jun-gen
one a-part, My ro - sa - ry, my ro - sa - ry!
sant à toi, Beau - coup trop vite el - les pas - saient!
Lie - be Glanz, Den Per - len gleich am Ro - sen - kranz.
poco rall.
L.H.
dolce

a tempo
mp
Each hour a pearl, each pearl a pray'r
Une pri-ère à cha-que grain
Wie sie, so reiht der Stun-den Zahl,
To still a heart in ab-sence
Pour cal-mer mon coeur aux a-
Ein lich-ter Kranz, sich je-des-
a tempo
mp
molto largamente
wrung: I tell each bead un to the end, And there a
bois, J'ar-rive ain-si jus-qu'à la fin, Mais là pend
mal Zur Ket-te von Ge-be-ten fromm.... Bis ich zum
dolce
f
a tempo p
cross is hung! O mem-o-ries that bless and
u-ne croix! O doux mo-ments si pleins d'é-
Kreu-ze komm'! Im Geist ent-schwund'ner Se-lig-
quasi arpeggio
p vibrato
dolcissimo

burn! O bar-ren gain and bit-ter loss!
moi, A vous tou-jours je dois pen-ser,
keit Küss' ich sie all', in stum-mem Leid,
patetico
mf sempre cresc.
I kiss each bead, and strive at last to learn To kiss the
J'em-bras-se cha-que grain jus-qu'à la croix, Tâ-chant d'ap-
Bis end-lich mir der Schmerz der letz-ten Stund' Drängt, O Ge-
f
f poco accel.
ff
Largo
pp
cross, sweet-heart! To kiss the cross.
prendre en-fin à l'em-bras-ser.
lieb-te(r), das Kreuz zum Mund.
poco accel.

Santa Lucia

Neapolitan Folk-Song

Andantino
p
Now 'neath the sil - ver moon O - cean is glow - ing,
O'er the calm bil - low Soft winds are blow - ing. Here balm - y
zeph - yrs blow, Pure joys in - vite_ us, And as we gent - ly row
All things de - light us. Hark, how the sail - or's cry Joy - ous - ly
f

p
ech-oes nigh. San-ta Lu-ci-a, San-ta Lu-ci-a.
f
Home of fair po-e-sy, Realm of pure har-mon-y, San-ta Lu-ci-a, San-ta Lu-ci-a.
mf

Serenade
Ständchen

English version by
Henry G. Chapman

Franz Schubert

Moderato
Piano
pp
Lei - se fle - hen mei - ne Lie - der durch die Nacht zu dir,
Soft - ly goes my song's en - trea - ty Thro' the night to thee,
in den stil - len Hain her - nie - der,
In the si - lent woods I wait thee,
Lieb - chen, komm zu mir.
Come, my love, to me.

Flü-sternd schlan - ke Wip-fel rau - schen in — des Mon - des Licht,
Tree-tops slen - der sough and whis - per In — the moon - light here,
in — des Mon - des Licht, des Ver-rä - thers feind-lich Lau - schen
in — the moon - light here, No un-friend - ly ear shall lis - ten,
fürch - te, Hol - de, nicht, fürch - te, Hol - de, nicht.
Dar - ling, have no fear, dar - ling, have no fear.
pp

Hörst die Nach - ti - gal - len schla - gen? Ach! sie fle - hen dich,
Hark! the night - in - gales are sing - ing, Ah, they plead with thee!
mit der Tö - ne sü - ssen Kla - gen
With their notes so sweet, so ring - ing,
fle - hen sie für mich.
They would plead for me.

Sie ver-steh'n des Bu-sens Seh - nen, ken-nen Lie - bes-schmerz,
Well they know a lov-er's long - ing, Know the pain of love,
pp
ken-nen Lie - bes-schmerz, rüh-ren mit den Sil-ber-tö - nen
know the pain of love, With their sil - ver-ton-ed voic - es
je - des wei - che Herz, je - des wei - che Herz.
Ten - der hearts they move, ten - der hearts they move.
Lass auch dir die Brust be-we - gen, Lieb - chen, hö - re mich!
Ah, let thine, as well, grow ten - der, Sweet - heart, why so coy?
cresc.

be - bend harr' ich dir ent-ge-gen,
An - xious, fe-ver'd, I a-wait thee,
komm, be-glü - cke mich!
Come and bring me joy,
komm, be-glü - cke mich,
come and bring me joy,
be - glü - - cke mich!
and bring me joy!
f
p
pp
dim.

She'll Be Comin' Round the Mountain

Brightly
1. She'll be com - in' round the moun - tain when she comes,
2. She'll be driv - in' six white hor - ses when she comes,
3. Oh, we'll all go out to meet her when she comes,
She'll be com - in' round the moun - tain when she comes,
She'll be driv - in' six white hor - ses when she comes,
Oh, we'll all go out to meet her when she comes,
She'll be steam - in' and a - puf - fin', Oh Lawd, She won't stop for
She'll be driv - in' six white hor - ses, She'll be driv - in' six white
We will kill the old red roos - ter, We will kill the old red
noth - in' She'll be com - in' round the moun - tain when she comes.
hor - ses, She'll be driv - in' six white hor - ses when she comes.
roos - ter, And we'll all have chick - en dump - lin's when she comes.
D.C.

The Sidewalks Of New York

"East Side, West Side"

Words and Music by
Chas. B. Lawlor and
James W. Blake

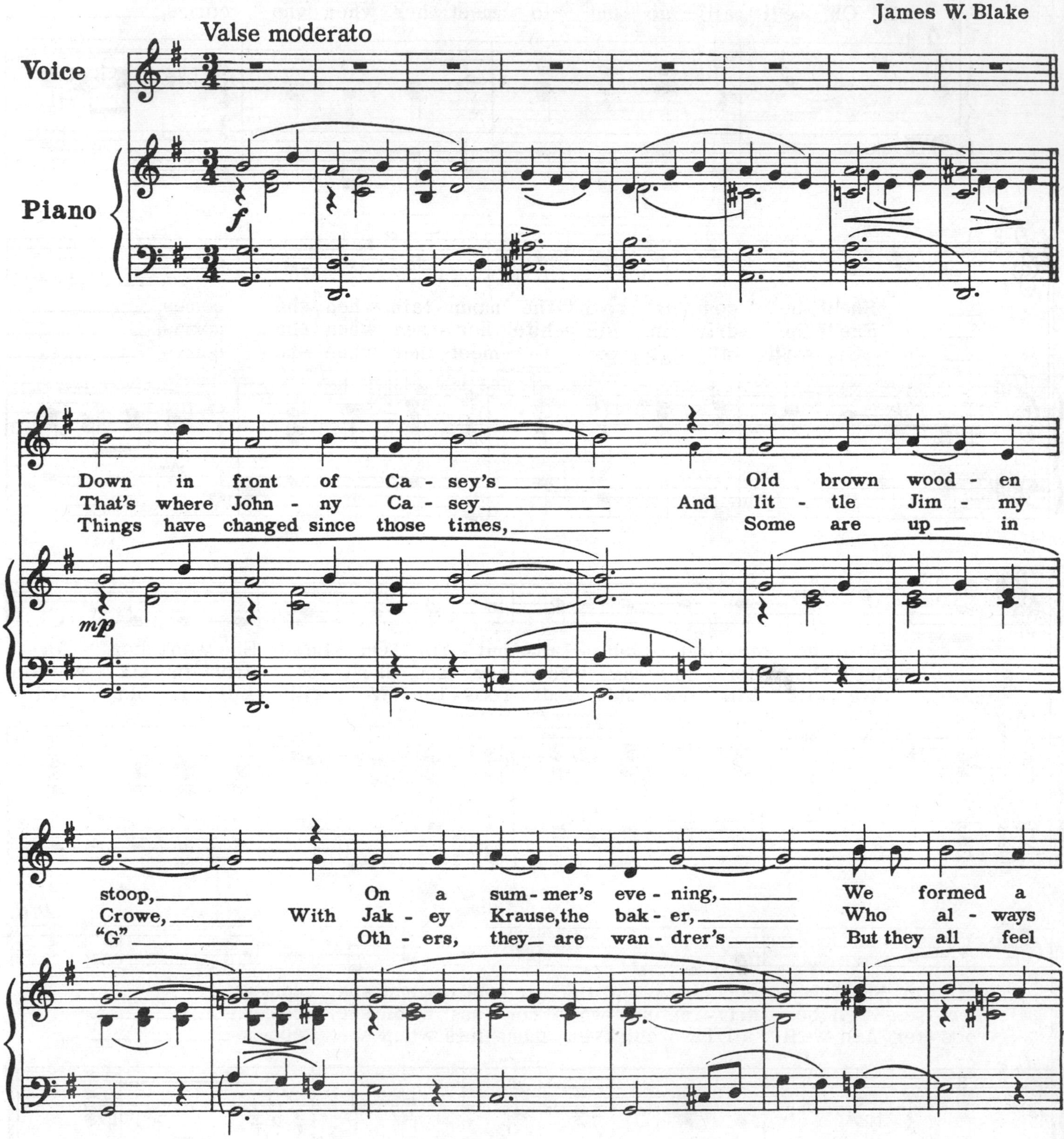
Valse moderato
Voice
Piano
f
mp
Down in front of Ca-sey's Old brown wood-en
That's where John-ny Ca-sey And lit-tle Jim-my
Things have changed since those times, Some are up in
stoop, On a sum-mer's eve-ning, We formed a
Crowe, With Jak-ey Krause, the bak-er, Who al-ways
"G" Oth-ers, they are wan-drer's But they all feel

Published, 1951, by The Boston Music Co.
Used by Permission

mer - ry group; Boys and girls to - geth - er,
had the dough; Pret - ty Nel - lie Shan - non, With a
just like me; They'd part with all they've got
we would sing and waltz, While To - ny played the
dude as light as cork, First picked up the
Could they once more walk With their best girl and
or - gan on The Side - walks Of New York.
waltz - step on The Side - walks Of New York.
have a twirl on The Side - walks Of New York.
Chorus
East side, West side all a - round the

town, The tots sang "ring a ros - ie," "Lon - don Bridge is
fall - ing down." Boys and girls to - geth - er,
Me and Ma-mie O - Rorke, Tripped the light fan - tas - tic
On The Side-walks Of New York. York.
1
2

Silver Threads Among The Gold

(Song and Chorus)

Music by
H. P. DANKS
arr. by Chester Wallis

Words by
EBEN E. REXFORD

Andante cantabile
mf
p
1. Dar - ling, I am grow-ing old,
2. When your hair is sil - ver white,
Sil - ver threads a-mong the gold, Shine up-on my brow to-day, Life is fad-ing fast a - way;
And your cheeks no long-er bright, With the ros-es of the May, I will kiss your lips and say;
But, my dar-ling, you will be, will be Al - ways young and fair to me,
Oh! my dar-ling, mine a - lone, a - lone, You have nev - er old-er grown.
Yes! my dar-ling, you will be Al - ways young and fair to me.
Yes! my dar-ling, mine a - lone, You have nev - er old-er grown.
ten.

CHORUS
SOPRANO
Dar-ling, I am grow-ing, grow-ing old, Sil-ver threads a-mong the gold,
ALTO
Dar-ling, I am grow-ing, grow-ing old, Sil-ver threads a-mong the gold, a-mong the gold,
TENOR
Dar-ling, I am grow-ing, grow-ing old, Sil-ver threads a-mong the gold, a-mong the gold,
BASS
Dar-ling, I am grow-ing, grow-ing old, Sil-ver threads a-mong the gold, a-mong the gold,
dim.
rall.
D.C.
Shine up-on my brow to-day; Life is fad-ing fast a-way.
Shine up-on my brow to-day; Life is fad-ing, fad-ing fast a-way.
Shine up-on my brow to-day; Life is fad-ing, fad-ing fast a-way.
Shine up-on my brow to-day, to-day, Life is fad-ing fast a way.
dim.
rall.
D.C.

3.

Love can never-more grow old,
Locks may lose their brown and gold;
Cheeks may fade and hollow grow;
But the hearts that love, will know
Never, never winter's frost and chill;
Summer warmth is in them still,
Never winter's frost and chill,
Summer warmth is in them still.

Chorus

4.

Love is always young and fair,
What to us is silver hair,
Faded cheeks or steps grown slow
To the hearts that beat below?
Since I kissed you, mine alone, alone,
You have never older grown,
Since I kissed you, mine alone,
You have never older grown.

Chorus

Sweet Genevieve

Music by
HENRY TUCKER
Arr. by CHESTER WALLIS

Words by
GEO. COOPER

Moderato
Voice
Piano
mf
p
O Gen-e-vieve, I'd give the world, To live a-gain the love-ly past! The rose of youth was dew-im-pearled; But now it with-ers in the blast. I see thy face in ev-'ry dream, My wak-ing thoughts are full of thee; Thy glance is in the star-ry beam That falls a-long the sum-mer sea.
Fair Gen-e-vieve, My ear-ly love, The years but make thee dear-er far! My heart shall nev-er, nev-er rove, Thou art my on-ly guid-ing star. For me the past has no re-gret, What-e'er the years may bring to me I bless the hour when first we met, The hour that gave me love and thee.

Soprano
O Gen-e-vieve, Sweet Gen-e-vieve, The days may come, the days may go, But
Alto
O Gen-e-vieve, Sweet Gen-e-vieve, The days may come, the days may go, But
Tenor
O Gen-e-vieve, Sweet Gen-e-vieve, The days may come, the days may go, But
Bass
O Gen-e-vieve, Sweet Gen-e-vieve, The days may come, the days may go, But
Piano
still the hands of mem-'ry weave The bliss-ful dreams of long a-go.
still the hands of mem-'ry weave The bliss-ful dreams of long a-go.
still the hands of mem-'ry weave The bliss-ful dreams of long a-go.
still the hands of mem-'ry weave The bliss-ful dreams of long a-go.

Sweet Rosie O'Grady

Words and Music by
MAUD NUGENT

Andante moderato
mf
rall.
p
Just down a-round the cor-ner of the street where I re-side, There
I nev-er shall for-get the day she prom-ised to be mine, As
p
a tempo
lives the cut-est lit-tle girl that I have ev-er spied; Her
we sat tell-ing love-tales, in the gold-en sum-mer time. 'Twas

name is Rose O' Gra-dy and, I don't mind tell-ing you, That
on her fing-er that I placed a small en-gage-ment ring, While
rit.
she's the sweet-est lit-tle Rose the gar-den ev-er grew.
in the trees, the lit-tle birds this song they seemed to sing:
rit.
CHORUS Valse moderato
p-mf
Sweet Ro-sie O' Gra--dy, My dear lit-tle
p-mf
Rose, She's my stead-y la--dy,

Most ev-'ry-one knows, And when we are
mar - ried, How hap-py we'll be;
I love sweet Ro-sie O' Gra - dy, And Ro-sie O'
Gra-dy loves me.
1.
2.
me.

Would God I were the tender apple-blossom

Katharine Tynan Hinkson

Londonderry Air
Arranged by Harrison Niel

Lento espressivo
Voice
Piano
p
p
p
Would God I were the tender apple-blossom That floats and falls from off the twisted bough, To lie and
Yea, would to God I were among the roses That lean to kiss you as you flow between, While on the
poco cresc.

faint . with - in your silk - en bos - om, With - in your
low - est branch a bud un - clos - es, A bud un -
poco rit.
a tempo
bos - om, as that does now! Or would I
clos - es to touch you, Queen. Nay, since you
a tempo
cresc.
were a lit - tle bur - nished ap - ple For you to
will not love, would I were grow - ing, A hap - py

pluck me glid - ing by so cold, While sun and
dai - sy in the gar - den path; That so your
f
shade your robe of lawn will dap - ple, Your robe of
sil - ver foot might press me go - ing, Might press me
f
8
rit.
lawn and your hair's spun gold.
go - ing ev - en un - to death!
rit. e dim.
8

Beautiful Dreamer

Arranged by
Jeffrey Marlowe

Words and Music by
Stephen C. Foster

Moderato
Piano
p
1. Beau - ti - ful dream - er, wake un - to me,
2. Beau - ti - ful dream - er, out on the sea,
Star-light and dew-drops are wait-ing for thee;
Mermaids are chanting the wild lor - e - lei;
Sounds of the rude world
O - ver the stream-let,
heard in the day,
va - pors are borne,
Lull'd by the moon-light have all pass'd a - way!
Wait-ing to fade at the bright com-ing morn.

Beau-ti-ful dream - er, queen of my song, List while I woo thee with
Beau-ti-ful dream - er, beam on my heart, E'en as the morn on the
soft mel - o - dy; Gone are the cares of life's bus - y throng,
stream-let and sea; Then will all clouds of sor - row de - part,
Beau-ti-ful dreamer, awake un-to me, Beau-ti-ful dreamer, a-wake un-to me!
rit.
cresc.
rit.

Chorus (optional) after each verse unaccompanied

Soprano & Alto
pp a tempo
1. Beau - ti - ful dream - er, queen of my song,
2. Beau - ti - ful dream - er, beam on my heart,
Tenor & Bass
pp a tempo
List while I woo thee with soft mel - o - dy; Gone are the cares of
E'en as the morn on the streamlet and sea; Then will all clouds of
life's bus - y throng,
sor - row de - part,
Beau - ti - ful dream - er, a - wake un - to
me,
mf
rit.
Beau - ti - ful dream - er, a - wake un - to me!
mf
rit.

De Camptown Races

or

"Gwine to run all night!"

Words and Music by
Stephen C. Foster

Tempo comodo
1. De Camp-town la - dies sing dis song, Doo-dah! doo-dah! De Camp-town race-track five miles long, Oh! doo - dah - day! I come down dar wid my hat cav'd in, Doo-dah! doo-dah! I go back home wid a pock-et-ful of tin, Oh! doo - dah - day!
2. De long-tail fil - ly, and de big black hoss, Doo-dah! doo-dah! Dey fly de track and dey both cut a-cross, Oh! doo - dah - day! De blind hoss stick-en in a big mud hole, Doo-dah! doo-dah! Can't touch bottom wid a ten - foot pole, Oh! doo - dah - day!
3. Old mul - ey cow come on to de track, Doo-dah! doo-dah! De bob - tail fling her o - ber his back, Oh! doo - dah - day! Den fly a - long like a rail - road car, Doo-dah! doo-dah! Runnin' a race wid a shoot - in' star, Oh! doo - dah - day!

Chorus
1-3. Gwine to run all night! Gwine to run all day! I'll
bet my mon-ey on de bob-tail nag, Some-bod-y bet on de bay.

Massa's in de Col', Col' Ground

Words and Music by
Stephen C. Foster

p cantabile
1. Roun' de mead-ows am a-ring-ing De dar-kies' mourn-ful song,
2. When de au-tumn leaves were fall-ing, When de days were cold, 'Twas
3. Mas-sa make de dar-kies love him, Cayse he was so kind,
While de mock-ing-bird am sing-ing, Hap-py as de day am long.
hard to hear old mas-sa call-ing, Cayse he was so weak and old.
Now, dey sad-ly weep a-bove him, Mourn-ing cayse he leave dem be-hind. I

Where de i - vy am a - creep - ing O'er de grass - y mound,
Now, de o - range tree am bloom - ing On de sand - y shore,
can - not work be - fore to - mor - row, Cayse de tear - drop flow, I
Dar old mas - sa am a - sleep - ing, Sleep - ing in de col', col' ground.
Now de summer days am com - ing, Mas - sa neb - ber calls no more.
try to drive a - way my sor - row, Pick - in' on de old ban - jo.
Chorus
f
1-3. Down in the corn - field Hear dat mourn - ful sound:
p
All de dar - kies am a - weep - ing, Mas - sa's in de col', col' ground.
calando

Jeanie with the light brown Hair

Arranged by
Jeffrey Marlowe

Words and Music by
Stephen C. Foster

Moderato
Piano
mf
p
1. I dream of Jea-nie, with the light brown hair, Borne, like a va - por,
2. I long for Jea-nie, with the gay dawn smile, Ra-diant in glad-ness,
3. I sigh for Jea-nie, but her light form strayed, Far from the fond hearts
on the sum-mer air; I see her trip-ping where the bright streams play,
warm with win-ning guile; I hear her mel-o - dies, like joys gone by,
'round her na-tive glade; Her smiles have van-ished, and her sweet songs flown,

Hap - py as the dai - sies that dance on her way.
Sigh - ing round my heart _ o'er the fond hopes that die.
Flit - ting like the dreams that have cheer'd us and gone.
p
Man - y were the wild notes her mer - ry voice would pour,
Sigh - ing like a night wind and sob - bing like the rain,
Now the nod - ding wild flow'rs may with - er on the shore,
p dolce
ad lib.
Man - y were the blithe birds that war - bled them o'er: Oh! I
Wail - ing for the lost one that comes not a - gain: Oh! I
While her gen - tle fin - gers will cull them no more: Oh! I

dream of Jea - nie with the light brown hair,
long for Jea - nie and my heart bows _ low,
sigh for Jea - nie with the light brown hair,
Cm
optional
Float - ing, like a va - por on the soft sum - mer air.
Nev - er more to find her where the bright wa - ters flow.
Float - ing, like a va - por on the soft sum - mer air.
8
p
1.
2.
D. S. last verse
8

My Old Kentucky Home

Words and Music by
Stephen C. Foster

Poco adagio
mf
1. The sun shines bright in my
2. They hunt no more for the
3. The head must bow, and the
mf
mf
old Ken-tuck-y home, 'Tis sum-mer, the dar-kies are gay; The
'pos-sum and the coon, On the meadow, the hill, and the shore; They
back will have to bend, Wher-ev-er the dar-kies may go: A
corn-top's ripe, and the meadow's all in bloom, While the birds make mu-sic all the
sing no more by the glimmer of the moon, On the bench by the old cab-in
few more days, and the trou-ble all will end, In the field where the su-gar-canes
day. The young folks roll on the lit-tle cab-in floor All
door. The day goes by like a shad-ow o'er the heart, With
grow. A few more days for to tote the wear-y load, No

mer-ry, all hap-py and bright, By'n by hard times comes a -
sor-row, where all was de - light: The time has come when the
mat-ter, 'twill nev-er be light, A few more days till we
knock-ing at the door, Then my old Ken-tuck-y Home, good - night!
dar-kies have to part; Then my old Ken-tuck-y Home, good - night!
tot-ter on the road; Then my old Ken-tuck-y Home, good - night!
rit.
Chorus
mf
1-3. Weep no more, my la - dy, Oh! weep no more to - day! We will
sing one song for the old Kentuck-y Home, For the old Kentuck-y Home, far a - way.

Nellie Was a Lady

Words and Music by
Stephen C. Foster

Adagio
1. Down on de Mis-sis-sip-pi float-ing, Long time I trab-ble on de way, All night de cot-ton-wood a-tot-ing, Sing for my true lub all de day.
2. Now I'm un-hap-py, and I'm weep-ing, Can't tote de cot-ton-wood no more; Last night, while Nel-lie was a-sleep-ing, Death came a-knock-in' at de door.
3. When I saw my Nel-lie in de morn-ing Smile till she o-pen'd up her eyes, Seem'd like de light ob day a-dawn-ing, Jist 'fore de sun be-gin to rise.
4. Down in de mead-ow, 'mong de clo-ber, Walk wid my Nel-lie by my side; Now all dem hap-py days am o-ber, Fare-well, my dark Vir-gin-ny bride.
Chorus
1-4. Nel-lie was a la-dy, Last night she died, Toll de bell for lub-ly Nell, My dark Vir-gin-ny bride.
rit. e dim.

Oh! Susanna

Words and Music by
Stephen C. Foster

Allegretto

1. I_ come from Al - a - ba-ma wid my ban-jo on my
2. I_ jumped a-board de tel-e-graph, And tra-beled down de
3. I_ had a dream de od-der night, When eb'-ry-ting was
knee; I'm gwine to Lou-si-an-na, My_ true love for to see. It_
rib-er, De Lec-tric flu-id mag-ni-fied, And killed five hun-dred Nig-ger. De
still; I_ thought I saw Su-san-na, A - com-ing down de hill. De
rain'd all night de day I left, The weath-er it was dry, The
bull-gine bust, de horse run off, I real-ly thought I'd die; I_
buck-wheat cake was in her mouth, De tear was in her eye; Says

sun so hot I froze to death; Su - san - na, don't you cry.
shut my eyes to hold my breath; Su - san - na, don't you cry.
I, I'm com - ing from de South, Su - san - na, don't you cry.
Chorus
1-4. Oh! Su - san - na! Oh, don't you cry for me, I've
come from Al - a - ba - ma, wid my ban - jo on my knee.

4. I soon will be in New-Orleans, And den I'll look all round,
And when I find Susanna, I'll fall upon the ground.
But if I do not find her, Dis darkie'l surely die,
And when I'm dead and buried, Susanna, don't you cry.

Old Black Joe

Words and Music by
Stephen C. Foster

Poco adagio

mf
mf
1. Gone are the days when my heart was young and gay,
2. Why do I weep when my heart should feel no pain?
3. Where are the hearts once so hap - py and so free? The
Gone are my friends from the cot - ton - fields a - way,
Why do I sigh that my friends come not a - gain?
chil - dren so dear, that I held up - on my knee?

Gone from this earth to a bet - ter land, I know, I
Griev - ing for forms now de - part - ed long a - go, I
Gone to the shore where my soul has long'd to go, I
poco rit.
hear their gen - tle voic - es call - ing, "Old Black Joe."
hear their gen - tle voic - es call - ing, "Old Black Joe."
hear their gen - tle voic - es call - ing, "Old Black Joe."
poco rit.
Chorus
mf
p
1-3. I'm com-ing, I'm com-ing, For my head is bend-ing
p
pp
mf
rit.
low, I hear those gen-tle voic-es call-ing, "Old Black Joe."
rit.

Old Folks at Home

Words and Music by
Stephen C. Foster

Moderato assai
espressivo
p
p espressivo
1. 'Way down up-on de Swa-nee rib-ber, Far, far a-way,
2. All round de lit-tle farm I wan-der'd When I was young,
3. One lit-tle hut a-mong de bushes, One dat I love,
Dere's wha' my heart am turn-ing eb-ber, Dere's wha' de old folks stay.
Den man-y hap-py days I squan-der'd, Man-y de songs I sung.
Still sad-ly to my mem-'ry rush-es, No mat-ter where I rove.

All up and down de whole cre - a - tion, Sad - ly I roam,
When I was play-ing wid my brud-der, Hap - py was I,
When will I see de bees a-hum-ming All round de comb?
Still long-ing for de old plan-ta-tion, And for de old folks at home.
Oh! take me to my kind old mud-der, Dere let me live and die.
When will I hear de ban-jo tum-ming, Down in my good old home?
Chorus
mf
1-3. All de world am sad and drear-y, Eb-'ry where I roam,
p
calando
Oh! dar-kies, how my heart grows wear-y, Far from de old folks at home.

Deep River

Negro Spiritual

Lento
Deep river, my
home is o - ver Jor - dan, Deep riv - er, Lord, I
want to cross o-ver in-to camp-ground. Deep
riv - er, my home is o - ver Jor - dan, Deep
mf

riv - er, Lord, I want to cross o-ver in-to camp-ground.
rit.
Oh, don't you want to go to that gos - pel feast, That
mf sub.
prom - ised land where all is peace, Deep
riv - er, Lord, I want to cross o-ver in-to camp-ground.

Go Down, Moses

Arranged by Estelle Liebling

Slowly and majestically
1. When Is - rael was in E - gypt's lan', Let my peo-ple go, Op - press'd so hard they could not stand, Let my people go.
2. Thus spoke the Lord, bold Mo - ses said, Let my peo-ple go, If not I'll smite your first-born dead, Let my people go.
Go down, Mo-ses, 'Way down in E-gypt's lan',_ Tell ole Pha - roah To let my peo-ple go. go.
ten.
colla voce
rall.

Nobody Knows the Trouble I See

Negro Spiritual

Moderato
No - bod - y knows the
mf
*
trou - ble I see, No - bod - y knows but Je - sus,
l.h.
2nd time only
No - bod - y knows the trou - ble I see, Glo - ry Hal - le - lu - jah. Some

* Small notes, designed to be played by left hand, are optional and may be omitted.

times I'm up, some - times I'm down, Oh, yes, Lord; Some -
f
slight retard
times I'm al - most to the ground,— Oh, yes, Lord.
a tempo
No - bod - y knows the trou - ble I see, No - bod - y knows but Je - sus,
mf
8
No - bo - dy knows the trou - ble I see, No - bod - y but Je - sus.

Oh! dem Golden Slippers!

Words and Music by
James A. Bland

Allegro
f
1. Oh, my gold - en slip - pers am a - laid a - way, Kase I
2. Oh, my ole ban - jo hangs on de wall, Kase it
3. So it's good - bye, chil - dren, I will have to go Whar de
f
don't 'spect to wear 'em till my wed - din' day, An' my long - tail'd coat, dat I
ain't been tuned since 'way last fall, But de darks all say we will
rain don't fall or de wind don't blow, An' yer ul - ster coats, why, yer
lov'd so well, I will wear up in de char - iot in de
hab a good time, When we ride up in de char - iot in de
will not need, When yer ride up in de char - iot in de

morn. An' my long white robe_ dat I bo't las' June, I'm_
morn. Dar's ole Brud-der Ben_ and_ Sis-ter Luce, Dey will
morn. But yer gold-en slip-pers must be nice and clean, And yer
gwine to git chang'd, Kase it fits too soon, An' de old gray hoss dat I
tel-e-graph de news to Un-cle Bac-co Juice, What a great camp-meet-in' der will
age must be_ Just_ sweet six-teen, An' yer white kid gloves yer will
used to drive, I will hitch him to de char-iot in de morn.
be dat day, When we ride up in de char-iot in de morn.
have to wear, When yer ride up in de char-iot in de morn.

Chorus
f
1-3. Oh, dem gold - en slip-pers! Oh, dem gold - en slip-pers!
Gold-en slip-pers I'se gwine to wear, be - kase dey look so neat,
Oh, dem gold - en slip-pers! Oh, dem gold - en slip-pers!
Gold-en slip-pers I'se gwine to wear, To walk de gold-en street. street.
1.
2.

Swing Low, Sweet Chariot

Negro Spiritual

mf
Swing low, sweet char - i - ot,
Com-in' for to car-ry me home,
Swing low, sweet char - i - ot,
Com-in' for to car-ry me home.
I look o - ver Jor-dan, and

what did I see,— Com-in' for to car-ry me home, A band of an-gels
f
mf
com-in' af-ter me,— Com-in' for to car-ry me home. Swing low, sweet
char - i - ot,— Com-in' for to car-ry me home, Swing low, sweet
char - i - ot,— Com-in' for to car-ry me home.

The flowers that bloom in the spring

from "The Mikado"

W. S. Gilbert

Arthur Sullivan
Arranged by Bryceson Treharne

Allegro giocoso
sf
mf
p
mf
1. The flow - ers that bloom in the spring, Tra - la, Breathe
2. The flow - ers that bloom in the spring, Tra - la, Have
prom - ise of mer - ry sun - shine— As we mer - ri - ly dance and we
noth - ing to do with the case. I've got to take un - der my

sing, Tra-la, We wel-come the hope that they bring, Tra-la, Of a
wing, Tra-la, A most un-at-trac-tive old thing, Tra-la, With a
sum-mer of ro-ses and wine, Of a sum-mer of ro-ses and
car-i-ca-ture of a face, With a car-i-ca-ture of a
wine. And that's what we mean when we say that a thing Is
face. And that's what I mean when I say, or I sing, Oh,

rall.
a tempo
wel- come as flow- ers that bloom in the spring,
both- er the flow- ers that bloom in the spring,
Tra la la la la, Tra
rall.
a tempo
la la la la, The flow - ers that bloom in the spring.
Oh, both - er the flow- ers of spring.
Tra
la la la la, Tra la la la la, Tra la la la la la!

I'm called Little Buttercup

from "H. M. S. Pinafore"

W. S. Gilbert

Arthur Sullivan
Arranged by Bryceson Treharne

Allegretto
f
mp
p
I'm called Lit - tle But - ter - cup, dear Lit - tle But - ter - cup,
Though I could nev - er tell why,
But still I'm called But - ter - cup,

poor Lit - tle But - ter - cup, Sweet Lit - tle But - ter - cup I!
I've snuff and to - bac - cy, and ex - cel - lent jack - y, I've
scis - sors, and watch - es, and knives; I've rib - bons and la - ces to
set off the fa - ces Of pret - ty young sweet - hearts and wives.

I've trea - cle and tof - fee, I've tea and I've cof - fee, Soft
tom - my and suc - cu - lent chops; I've chick - ens and
co - nies, and pret - ty po - lo - nies, And ex - cel - lent
rall.
a tempo
pep - per - mint drops. Then buy of your But - ter - cup,
rall.
a tempo

dear Lit - tle But - ter - cup, Sail - ors should nev - er be
shy; So buy of your But - ter - cup, poor Lit - tle
But - ter - cup, Come, of your But - ter - cup, buy.

Poor wandering one!

from "The Pirates of Penzance"

W. S. Gilbert

Arthur Sullivan
Arranged by Bryceson Treharne

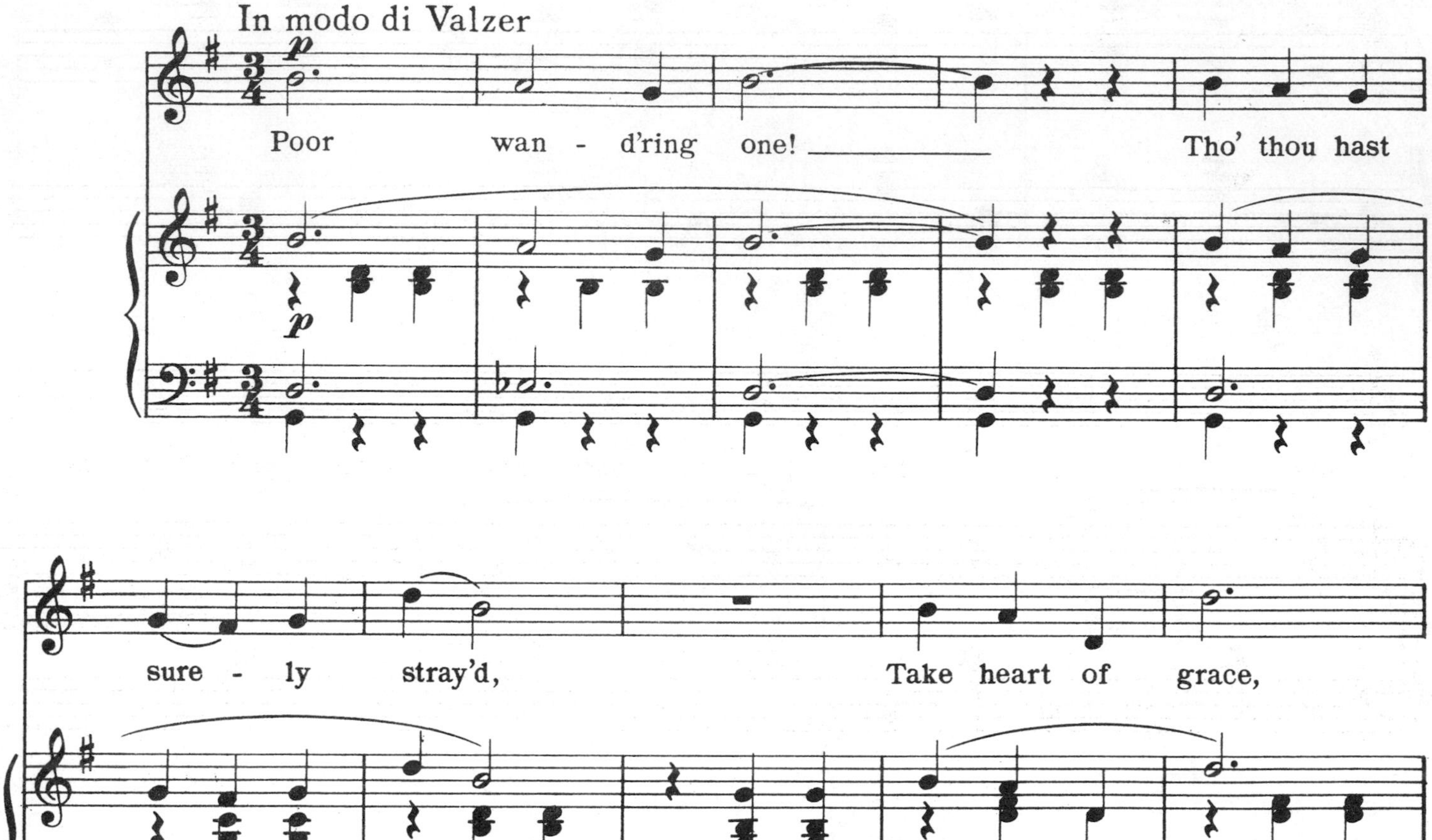
In modo di Valzer
p
Poor wan - d'ring one! Tho' thou hast
sure - ly stray'd, Take heart of grace,
Thy steps re - trace, Poor wan - d'ring one!
rall.

a tempo
Poor wan - d'ring one! If such poor love as mine
a tempo
Can help thee find True peace of mind— Why, take it, it— is
thine! Take heart, no dan-ger low'rs; Take
f
f
an - y heart— but ours! Take heart, fair days will shine; Take

f
an - y heart — take mine! Take heart, no dan-ger
mf
low'rs; Take — an - y heart — but ours! Take heart,
p
fair days will shine, Take an - y heart — take mine! Ah! Ah!
Ah! Ah!
cresc.

a tempo
p
Poor wan - d'ring one! Tho' thou hast sure - ly stray'd,
p
a tempo
Take heart of grace, Thy steps re - trace, — Poor
a tempo
wan - d'ring one! Ah, ah, Ah, ah, ah,
a tempo
Ah, ah! Ah, ah, ah, Fair days will shine.

Take heart!
pp
Take mine! Take heart!

Take mine!
f a tempo
mf
tr
Ah!
ah!
ah!
ah!
ff
Ped.
*

When I was a lad

from "H. M. S. Pinafore"

W. S. Gilbert

Arthur Sullivan
Arranged by Bryceson Treharne

Allegro non troppo
f
mp
p
1. When I was a lad I served a term As
2. As of-fice boy I made such a mark That they
of-fice boy to an at-tor-ney's firm, I cleaned the win-dows and I
gave me the post__ of a jun-ior clerk, I served the writs with a

f
swept the floor, And I pol ished up the han-dle of the big front door. He
smile so bland, And I cop-ied all the let-ters in a big round hand. He
f
pol-ished up the han-dle of the big front door. I
cop-ied all the let-ters in a big round hand. I
pol-ished up that han-dle So care-ful-lee, That
cop-ied all the let-ters in a hand so free, That
f
now I am the rul-er of the Queen's Na-vee. He
now I am the rul-er of the Queen's Na-vee. He
f

pol - ished up that han - dle So care - ful - lee, That
cop - ied all the let - ters in a hand so free, That
now he is the rul - er of the Queen's Na - vee.
now he is the rul - er of the Queen's Na - vee.
mp
3. In serv - ing writs I made such a name That an
4. Of leg - al know-ledge I ac-quired such a grip That they
p
ar - ti - cled clerk I soon be - came; I
took me in - to the part - ner - ship, And that

wore clean col - lars and a bran' new suit For the
jun - ior part - ner - ship, I ween, Was the
f
pass ex - am - i - na - tion at the In - sti - tute. For the
on - ly ship that I ev - er had seen. Was the
f
pass ex - am - i - na - tion at the In - sti - tute. That
on - ly ship he ev - er had seen. But
pass ex - am - i - na - tion did so well for me That
that kind of ship so suit - ed me That

f
now I am the rul - er of the Queen's Na - vee, That
now I am the rul - er of the Queen's Na - vee, But
f
pass ex - am - i - na - tion did so well for he That
that kind of ship so suit - ed he That
now he is the rul - er of the Queen's Nav - ee.
now he is the rul - er of the Queen's Nav - ee.
mp
5. I grew so rich that I was sent By a
6. Now lands-men all, who - ev-er you may be, If you
p

pock - et bor-ough in - to Par - lia - ment, I al - ways vot - ed at my
want to rise__ to the top of the tree, If your soul is - n't fet - tered to an
par - ty's call, And I nev - er thought of think - ing for my - self at all. He
of - fice stool, Be care - ful to be guid - ed by this gold - en rule— Be
f
nev - er thought of think - ing for him - self at all. I
care - ful to be guid - ed by this gold - en rule— Stick
thought so lit - tle, they re - ward - ed me, By
close to your desks and nev - er go to sea, And you

f
making me the ruler of the Queen's Navee. He
all may be rulers of the Queen's Navee. Stick
thought so little, they rewarded he By
close to your desks and never go to sea, And you
making him the ruler of the Queen's Navee.
all may be rulers of the Queen's Navee.
1.
2.
Queen's Navee.

Willow, tit-willow

from "The Mikado"

W. S. Gilbert

Arthur Sullivan
Arranged by Bryceson Treharne

Andante espressivo
mp
p
1. On a
tree by a riv-er a lit-tle tom-tit Sang "Wil-low, tit-wil-low, tit-
wil-low!" And I said to him,"Dick-y-bird, why do you sit Sing-ing,

'Wil - low, tit-wil - low, tit - wil - low?' Is it weak - ness of in - tel - lect,
bird - ie?" I cried, "Or a rath - er tough worm in your
lit - tle in - side?" With a shake of his poor lit - tle
head he re - plied, "Oh, wil - low, tit-wil - low, tit - wil - low!"

2. He slapped at his chest as he
sat on that bough, Sing-ing, "Wil-low, tit-wil-low, tit-wil-low!" And a
cold per-spi-ra-tion be-span-gled his brow, Oh, wil-low, tit-wil-low, tit-
wil-low! He_ sobbed and he sighed and a gur-gle he gave, Then he

plunged him-self in - to the bil-low-y wave, And an ech - o a-rose from the
su - i-cide's grave— "Oh, wil-low, tit-wil-low, tit - wil-low!"
3. Now I feel just as sure as I'm sure that my name Is-n't
Wil-low, tit-wil-low, tit-wil-low,_ That 'twas blight-ed af-fec-tion that

made him ex-claim, "Oh, wil-low, tit-wil-low, tit-wil-low!" And if
you re-main cal-lous and ob-du-rate, I shall per-ish as he did, and
you will know why, Though I prob-a-bly shall not ex-
claim as I die, "Oh, wil-low, tit-wil-low, tit-wil-low!"
pp

Au Clair de la Lune

Moderato
Au clair de la lu - ne, Mon a - mi Pier - rot,
Prê-te-moi ta plu - me Pour é-crire un mot.
Ma chan-delle est mor - te,
Je n'ai plus de feu;
Ou-vre-moi ta por - te Pour l'a-mour de Dieu.

Au clair de la lune,
Pierrot répondit:
Je n'ai pas de plume,
Je suis dans mon lit.

Va chez la voisine,
Je crois qu'elle y est,
Car dans sa cuisine,
On bat le briquet.

En revenant d'Auvergne

Con moto
En re-ve-nant d'Au - ver - gne,
En re-ve-nant d'Au - ver - gne,
En re-ve-nant d'Au - ver - gne, d'Au - ver-gne, mon pa - ys.

Pas-sant par la Li-ma-gne, Pas-sant par la Li-ma-gne,
Pas-sant par la Li-ma-gne, D'la Li-magne à Pa-ris. Chan
Fine
tant la Sa-voy-ar-de, Dan-sant la Mon-ta-gnar-de. Eh
gai Co-co! Eh gai Co-co! Eh ve-nez voir la dan-se
Du pe-tit mar-mot. Eh ve-nez voir la dan-se Du pe-tit mar-
mot, Du pe-tit mar-mot, Du pe-tit mar-mot.
f
f
D.C. al Fine

Frère Jacques *)

Frè - re Jac - ques, Frè - re Jac - ques, dor - mez -
Frè - re
vous? Dor - mez - vous? Son - nez les ma - ti - nes, Son - nez les ma -
Jac - ques, Frè - re Jac - ques, dor - mez - vous? Dor - mez -
Frè - re Jac - ques, Frè - re
ti - nes, Din, din, don! Din, din, don! Frè - re
vous? Son - nez les ma - ti - nes, Son - nez les ma - ti - nes, Din, din,
Jac - ques, dor - mez - vous? Dor - mez - vous? Son - nez les ma -
Jac - ques, Frè - re Jac - ques, dor - mez - vous? Dor - mez - vous?
don! Din, din, don! Frè - re Jac - ques, Dor - mez - vous?
ti - nes, Son - nez les ma - ti - nes, Din, din, don! Din, din, don!

*) This song may be rendered as a Three-part Round.

La Bergère

Allegretto
1. Il é-tait un' ber-gè-re, Et ron, ron, ron, Pe-tit pa-ta-pon, Il é-tait un' ber-gè-re Qui gar-dait ses mou-tons, ron, ron, Qui gar-dait ses mou-tons.
p
mf

2.

Elle fit un fromage,
Et ron, ron, ron, petit patapon,
Elle fit un fromage
Du lait de ses moutons,
Ron, ron,
Du lait de ses moutons.

3.

Le chat qui la regarde,
Et ron, ron, ron, petit patapon,
Le chat qui la regarde
D'un petit air fripon,
Ron, ron,
D'un petit air fripon.

4.

Si tu y mets la patte,
Et ron, ron, ron, petit patapon,
Si tu y mets la patte,
Tu auras du bâton,
Ron, ron,
Tu auras du bâton.

5.

Il n'y mit pas la patte,
Et ron, ron, ron, petit patapon,
Il n'y mit pas la patte,
Il y mit le menton,
Ron, ron,
Il y mit le menton.

6.

La bergère en colère,
Et ron, ron, ron, petit patapon,
La bergère en colère,
A tué son chaton,
Ron, ron,
A tué son chaton.

Le Pont d'Avignon

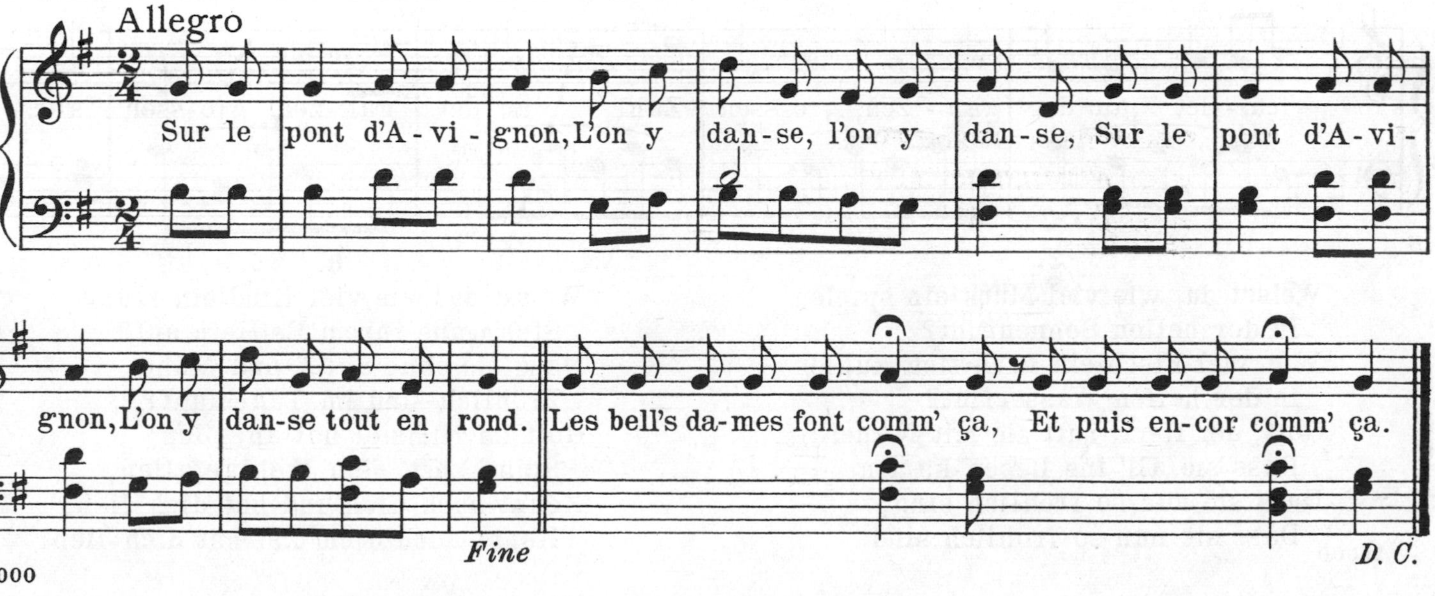

Allegro
Sur le pont d'A-vi-gnon, L'on y dan-se, l'on y dan-se, Sur le pont d'A-vi-gnon, L'on y dan-se tout en rond. Les bell's da-mes font comm' ça, Et puis en-cor comm' ça.
Fine
D. C.

O, du lieber Augustin

Lustig
O, du lie - ber Au - gu - stin, Au - gu - stin, Au - gu - stin,
o, du lie-ber Au-gu-stin, Al-les ist hin! Geld ist weg, Geld ist weg,
Al - les weg, al - les weg! O, du lie-ber Au - gu - stin, Al - les ist hin!

Weisst du, wie viel Sternlein stehen

Ruhig
p
Weisst du, wie viel Stern-lein ste-hen an dem blau-en Him-mels-zelt?
Weisst du, wie viel Wölk-lein ge-hen weit-hin ü-ber al-le Welt?
Gott, der Herr, hat sie ge - zäh - let, dass ihm auch nicht ei - nes
feh - let an der gan - zen, gro - ssen Zahl, an der gan-zen, gro-ssen Zahl.

2.

Weisst du, wie viel Mücklein spielen
In der hellen Sonnenglut?
Wie viel Fischlein auch sich kühlen
In der hellen Wasserflut?
Gott, der Herr, ruft sie mit Namen,
Dass sie all' ins Leben kamen,
Dass sie nun so fröhlich sind,
Dass sie nun so fröhlich sind.

3.

Weisst du, wie viel Kindlein frühe
Steh'n aus ihrem Bettlein auf?
Dass sie ohne Sorg' und Mühe
Fröhlich sind im Tageslauf?
Gott im Himmel hat an allen
Seine Lust, sein Wohlgefallen,
Kennt auch dich und hat dich lieb,
Kennt auch dich und hat dich lieb.

Dickory, dickory, dock

Allegro
mf
Dick-o-ry, dick-o-ry, dock; The mouse ran up the clock; The clock struck One, The mouse ran down; Dick-o-ry, dick-o-ry, dock.
fz
ten.
p
sfz

Ding dong bell

Ding dong bell! Pus-sy's in the well! Who put her in?
Lit-tle Tom-my Lin. Who pulled her out? Lit-tle Tom-my Stout. What a

naugh - ty boy was that, To drown poor pus - sy cat, Who
ne'er did an - y harm, But killed all the mice in — his fa - ther's barn.

Hey, diddle diddle

Allegro
Hey, did-dle did-dle, The cat and the fid-dle, The cow jump'd o-ver the moon; — The
lit-tle dog laughed To see such sport, And the dish ran af-ter the spoon. —

Georgie Porgie

Allegretto moderato

mp sempre legato
Geor - gie Por - gie, pud - ding and pie, Kiss'd the girls and made them cry;
mp
f
dim.
When the girls came out to play, Geor - gie Por - gie ran a - way.
f
dim.

Humpty Dumpty

Allegretto

p
Hump - ty Dump - ty sat on a wall, Hump - ty Dump - ty
p
cresc.
had a great fall: All the king's hors - es, and all the king's men,
cresc.

Could-n't put Hump-ty Dump-ty to-geth-er a-gain.

I had a little nut-tree

I had a lit-tle nut-tree, no-thing would it bear
mf
But a sil-ver nut-meg and a gold-en pear; The King of Spain's daugh-ter
came to vis-it me, And all for the sake of my lit-tle nut-tree.

I love little Pussy

Andante non troppo
p With tenderness
I love lit-tle Pus-sy, her coat is so warm, And
if I don't hurt her, she'll do me no harm. I'll sit by the fire and
give her some food, And Pus-sy will love me, be-cause I am good.
cresc.
dim. e ritard.
p
fz
pp

Jack and Jill

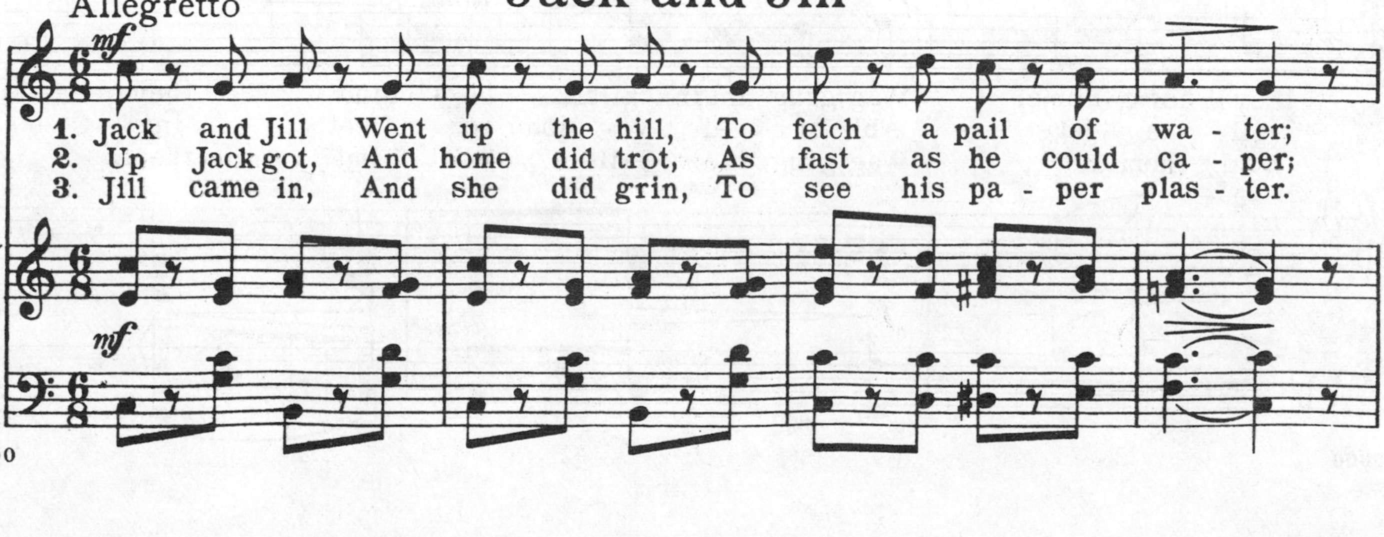

1. Jack and Jill Went up the hill, To fetch a pail of wa-ter;
2. Up Jack got, And home did trot, As fast as he could ca-per;
3. Jill came in, And she did grin, To see his pa-per plas-ter.

Jack fell down, And broke his crown, And Jill __ came tum-bling af - ter.
Went to bed, To mend his head, With vin-e-gar and brown pa-per.
Moth - er, vex'd, Did whip her next, For caus - ing Jack's dis - as - ter.
ten.

Little Bo-Peep

Andante quasi Allegretto

p
1. Lit - tle Bo - Peep has lost her sheep, And can't tell where to find them; Leave them a - lone, __ and they'll come home, Wag-ging their tails __ be - hind them.
2. Lit - tle Bo - Peep fell fast a - sleep, And dreamt she heard them bleat - ing; When she a - woke, __ 'twas all a joke: Ah! cru - el vi - sion so fleet - ing.
3. Then __ up she took her lit - tle crook, De - ter - mined for __ to find them; What was her joy to be - hold them nigh, Wag-ging their tails __ be - hind them.
cresc.
f
dim.

Little Jack Horner or Little Miss Muffet

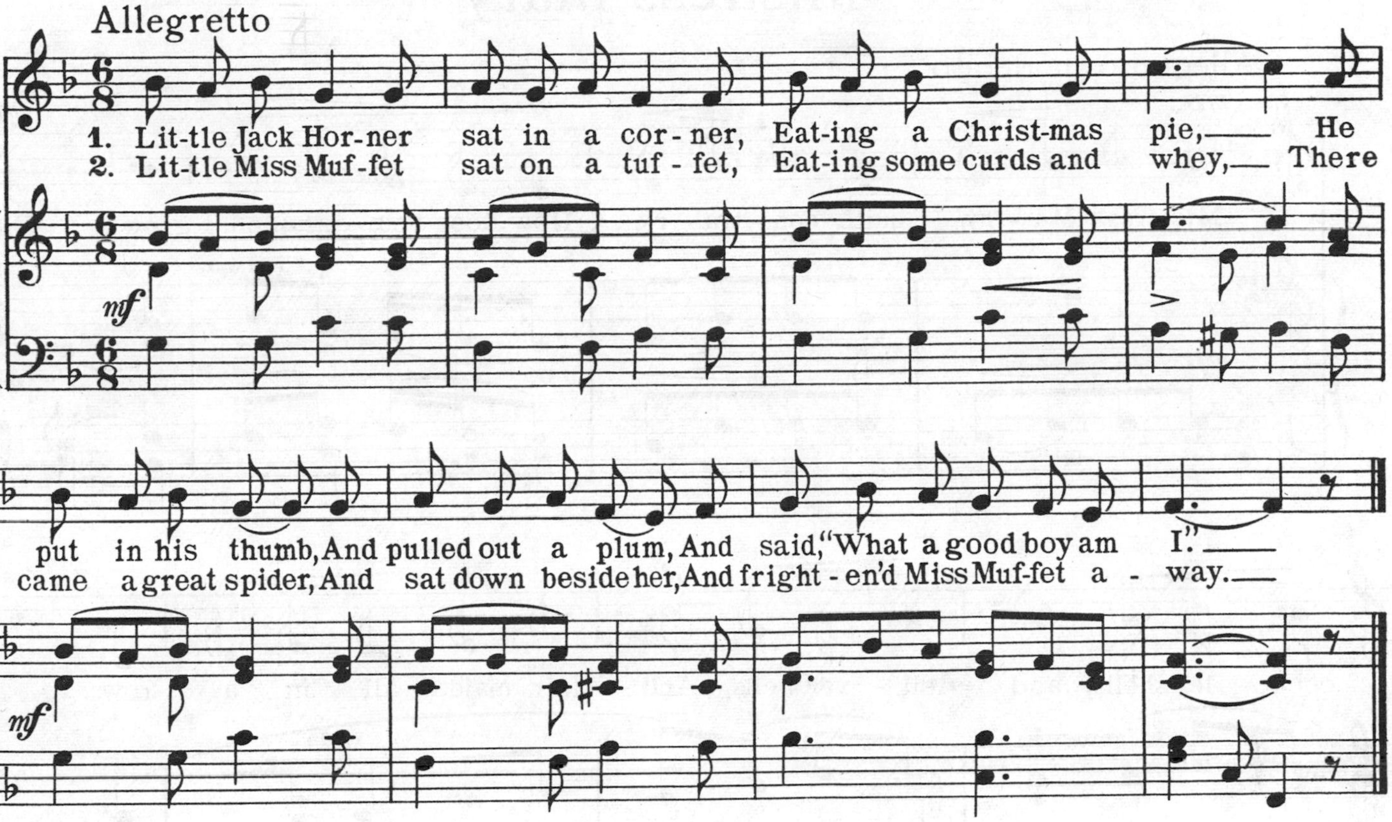
Allegretto
1. Lit-tle Jack Hor-ner sat in a cor-ner, Eat-ing a Christ-mas pie,—— He
2. Lit-tle Miss Muf-fet sat on a tuf-fet, Eat-ing some curds and whey,—— There
mf
put in his thumb, And pulled out a plum, And said, "What a good boy am I."——
came a great spider, And sat down beside her, And fright-en'd Miss Muf-fet a-way.——
mf

Mary had a little lamb

1. Ma-ry had a lit-tle lamb, lit-tle lamb, lit-tle lamb,
2. And ev-'ry-where that Ma-ry went, Ma-ry went, Ma-ry went, And
3. It fol-lowed her to school one day, school one day, school one day, It
4. It made the chil-dren laugh and play, laugh and play, laugh and play, It
5. And so the teach-er turned him out, turned him out, turned him out, And
6. And wait-ed pa-tient-ly a-bout, ly a-bout, ly a-bout, And
legato
con Ped.
Ma-ry had a lit-tle lamb, Its fleece was white as snow.
ev-'ry-where that Ma-ry went, The lamb was sure to go.
fol-lowed her to school one day, Which was a-gainst the rule.
made the chil-dren laugh and play, To see a lamb at school.
so the teach-er turned him out, But still he lin-gered near.
wait-ed pa-tient-ly a-bout Till Ma-ry did ap-pear.
Ped. *

Mistress Mary

Allegretto moderato
Mis-tress Ma - ry, quite con - tra - ry, How does your gar - den grow? With
cock - le-shells, and sil - ver bells, And fair maids all in a row.

Old King Cole

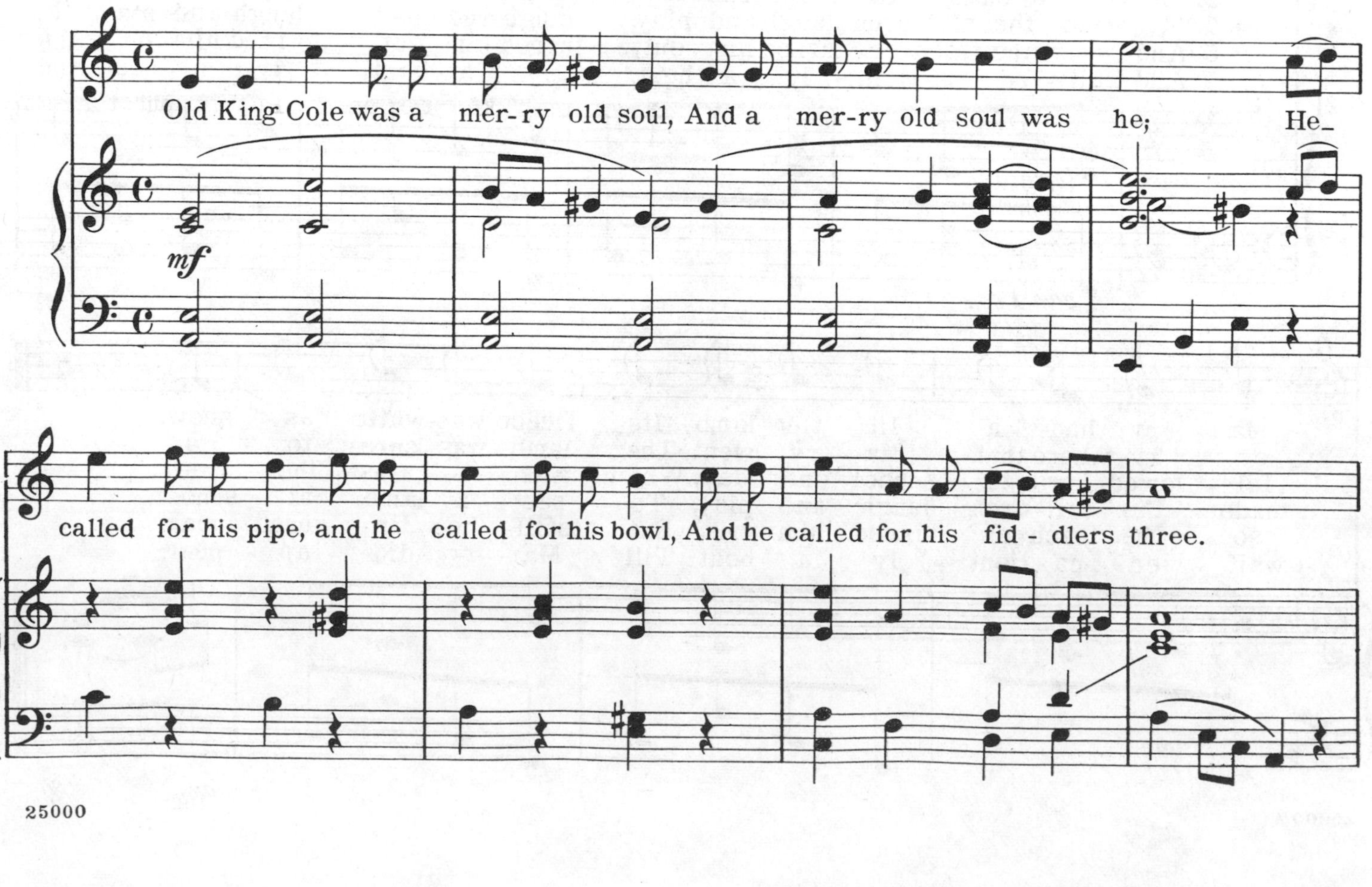

Old King Cole was a mer-ry old soul, And a mer-ry old soul was he; He
called for his pipe, and he called for his bowl, And he called for his fid - dlers three.

Ev - 'ry — fid - dler had a — fid - dle, And a ver - y fine fid - dle had he.
Twee - dle dee, tweedle dee, tweedle dee, tweedle dee,
Twee - dle dee, tweedle dee, went the fid - dlers three,
O there's none so — rare as — can com - pare

Polly, put the kettle on

Pol - ly, put the ket - tle on, Pol - ly, put the ket - tle on, Pol - ly, put the
ket - tle on, We'll all have tea. Su - key, take it off a - gain, Su - key, take it

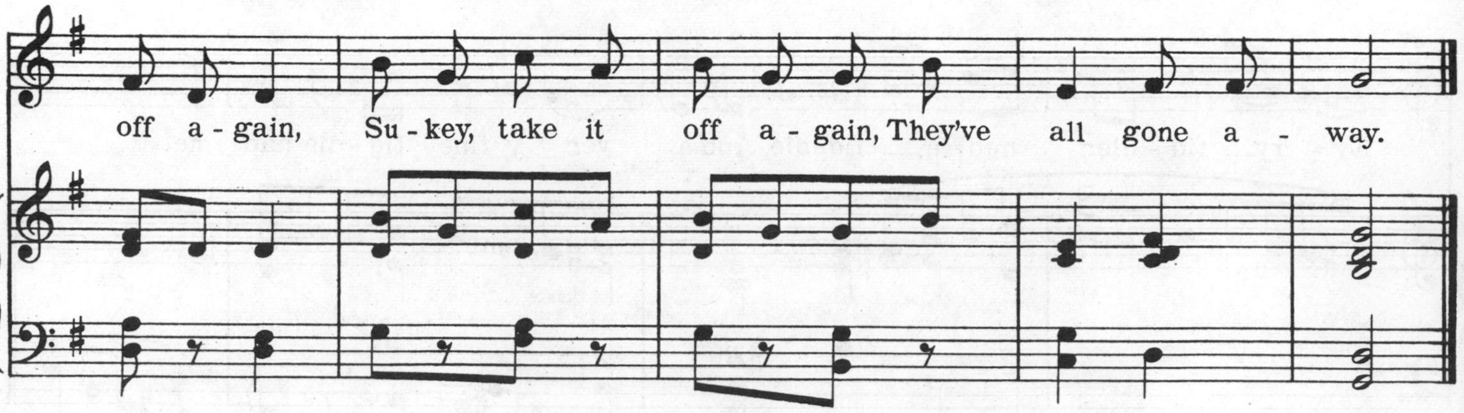

off a-gain, Su-key, take it off a-gain, They've all gone a - way.

Pop! goes the weasel!

All a-round the cob-bler's bench The mon-key chased the wea - sel; The
mf
mon-key tho't 'twas all_ in fun, Pop! goes the wea-sel! I've no time to wait or sigh, No
3
pa-tience to wait till by and by; Kiss me quick, I'm off, good-bye, Pop! goes the wea-sel!
3

Three Blind Mice

Three blind mice,— three blind mice,— See how they run,— see how they run!— They all run aft - er the farm - er's wife. She cut off their tails with a carv - ing knife. Did you ev - er see such a sight in your life As three blind mice.

Old MacDonald Had a Farm

Old Mac-Don-ald had a farm, Ee-i, ee-i, O; And
on this farm he had a chick, duck, sheep, cow, Ee-i, ee-i, O. With a
chick, quack, baa, moo, chick here and a chick chick there, Here a chick, there a chick,
here and there a chick, chick, Old Mac-Don-ald had a farm, Ee-i, ee-i, O.

Tom, the piper's son

Allegretto e marcato
Tom, Tom, the pip-er's son, Stole a pig, and a-way he run! The
pig was eat, And Tom was beat, Which sent him howl-ing down the street.

Twinkle, twinkle, little star

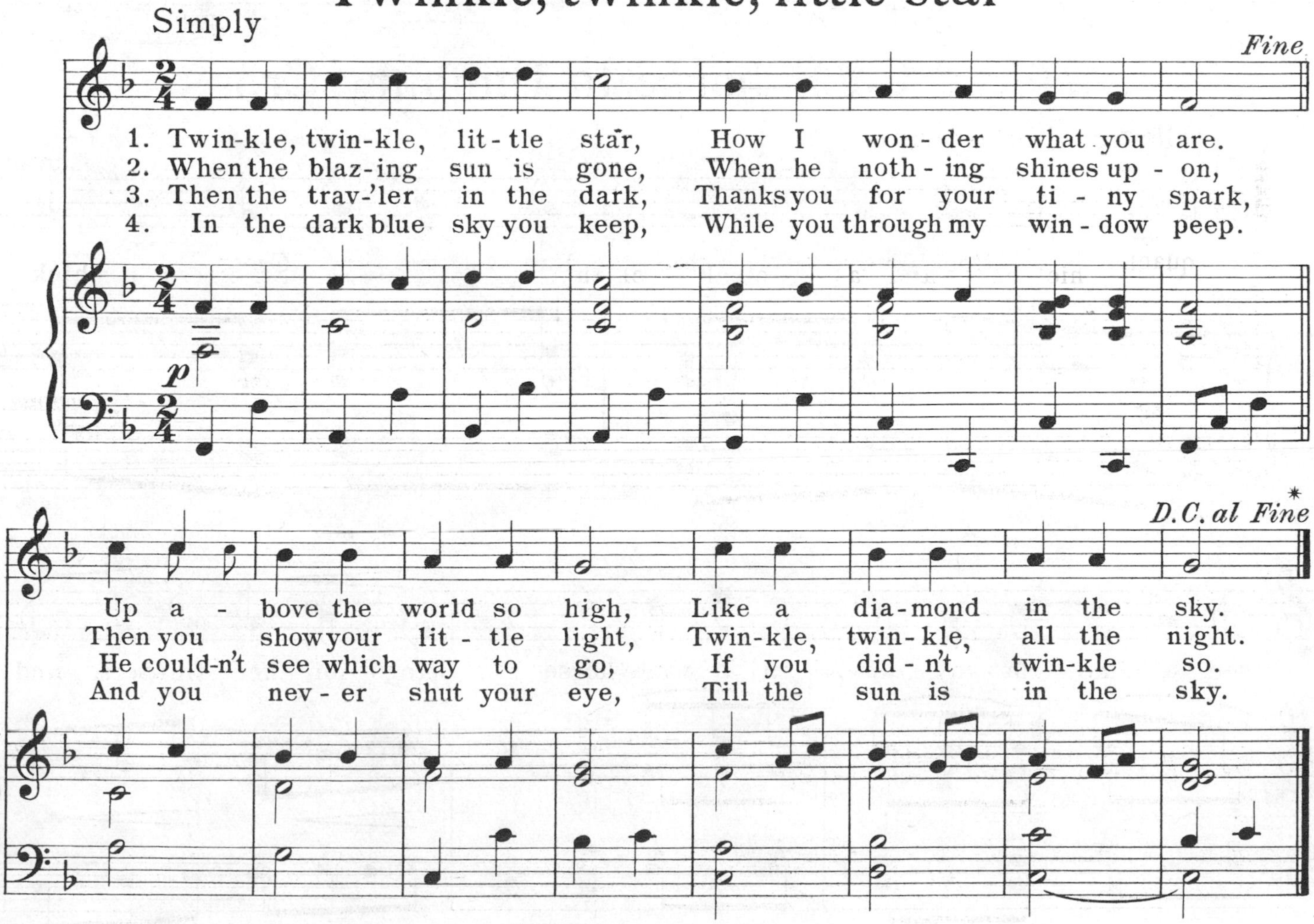

Simply
Fine
1. Twin-kle, twin-kle, lit-tle star, How I won-der what you are.
2. When the blaz-ing sun is gone, When he noth-ing shines up-on,
3. Then the trav-'ler in the dark, Thanks you for your ti-ny spark,
4. In the dark blue sky you keep, While you through my win-dow peep.
D.C. al Fine*
Up a-bove the world so high, Like a dia-mond in the sky.
Then you show your lit-tle light, Twin-kle, twin-kle, all the night.
He could-n't see which way to go, If you did-n't twin-kle so.
And you nev-er shut your eye, Till the sun is in the sky.

*For all four verses, always repeat the words of Verse I (to Fine.)

Pussy-cat, pussy-cat

Allegro

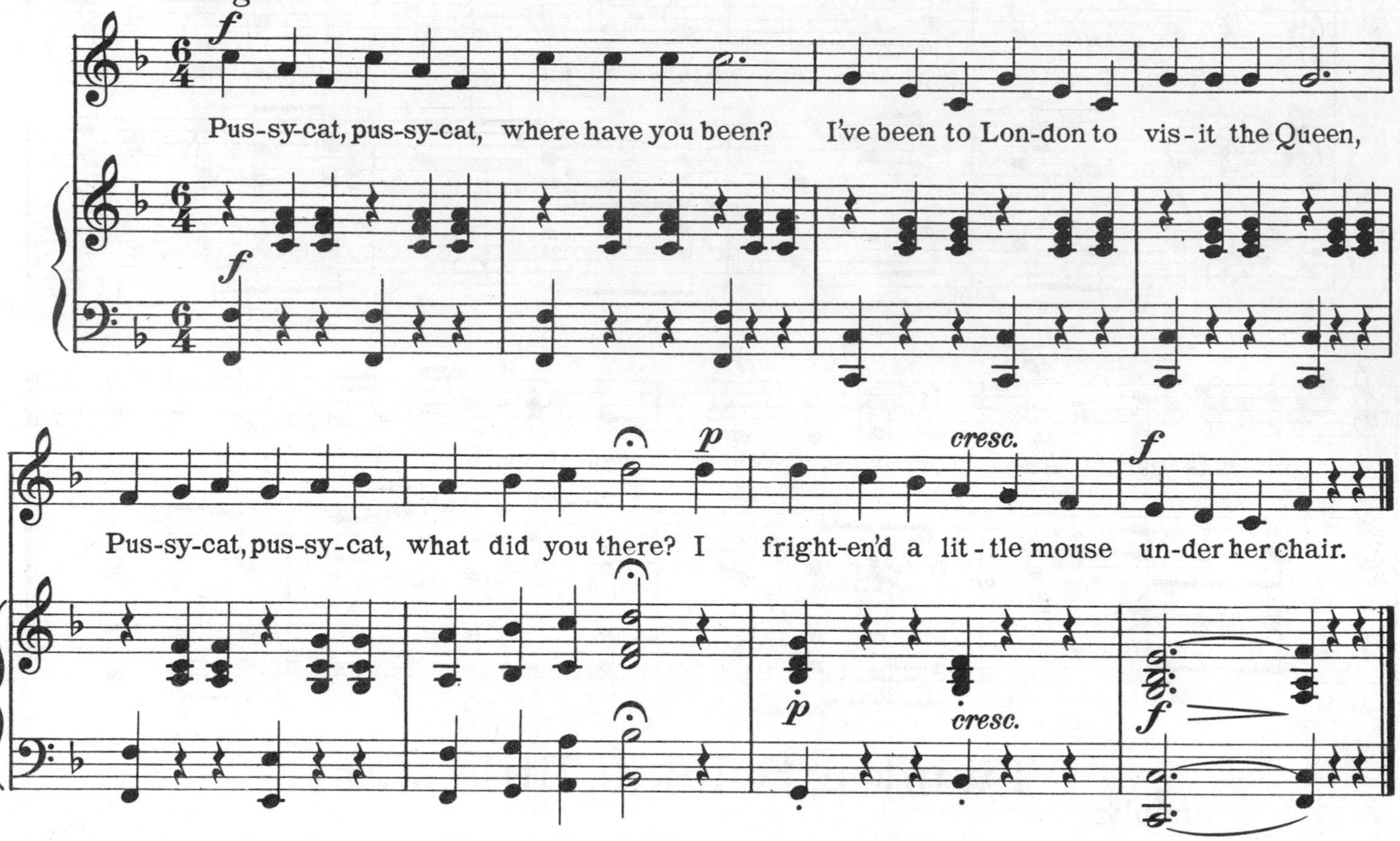

Pus-sy-cat, pus-sy-cat, where have you been? I've been to Lon-don to vis-it the Queen,
Pus-sy-cat, pus-sy-cat, what did you there? I fright-en'd a lit-tle mouse un-der her chair.
cresc.
cresc.

Ride a Cock-horse to Banbury Cross

Allegretto con spirito

see a fine la-dy up-on a white horse; Rings on her fin-gers, and

f
bells on her toes, She shall have mu - sic wher - ev - er she goes.
f

Sing a song of sixpence

1. Sing a song of six - pence, a pock - et full of rye;
2.The king was in his count - ing - house, count - ing out his mon - ey; The
Four - and-twen - ty black-birds baked in a pie; When the pie was o - pen'd the
queen was in the par - lor eat - ing bread and hon - ey; The maid was in the gar - den
birds be - gan to sing, Was - n't that a dain - ty dish to set be - fore the king?
hang - ing out her clothes, When up — came a black - bird and pecked off her nose.

Where has my little dog gone

Folk Tune

Oh where, oh where has my lit - tle dog gone? Oh
where, oh where can he be? With his ears cut short and his
tail cut long, Oh where, oh where can he be?

Little Tommy Tucker

J. W. Elliot

Lit - tle Tom - my Tuck - er, Sing for your sup - per.

What shall he sing for? White bread and but - ter. How can he cut it With -
out an - y knife? How can he mar - ry With - out an - y wife?

Simple Simon

J. W. Elliot

1 Sim - ple Si - mon met a pie - man, Go - ing to the fair. Said
2 Pie - man said to Sim - ple Si - mon: "Show me first your pen - ny." Said
Sim - ple Si - mon to the pie - man: "Let me taste your ware."
Sim - ple Si - mon to the pie - man: "'Deed I have not an - y."

The Holy City

F. E. Weatherly

Stephen Adams

Andante moderato
Voice
Piano
p
Last
night I lay a-sleep-ing, There came a dream so fair: I
stood in old Je-ru-sa-lem, Be-side the tem-ple there; I

Published, 1942 by Boston Music Co.
Used by Permission

25000

mf
heard the chil-dren sing-ing, And ev-er as they sang, Me-
thought the voice of an-gels, From heav'n in an-swer rang; Me-
mf cresc.
cantabile
thought the voice of an-gels From
f
rall.
heav'n in an-swer rang. "Je-
rall.

a tempo
ru - sa-lem! Je - ru - sa-lem!
p a tempo
Lift up your gates and sing, Ho - san - na in_the
mf
high - est, Ho - san - na__ to your King!"
colla voce
ff
dim.
p
And

then me-thought my dream was chang'd, The streets no long - er rang,
p
Hush'd were the glad Ho-san-nas The lit - tle chil-dren sang; The
sun grew dark with mys - ter - y, The morn was cold and chill, As the
mf
p
cresc.
shad - ow of a cross a - rose Up - on a lone - ly hill, As the
mf cresc.

cantabile
shad - ow of a cross a - rose Up -
f
rall.
on a lone - ly hill.
rall.
a tempo
"Je - ru - sa - lem! Je -
p a tempo
ru - sa - lem!" Hark! how the an - gels sing: Ho -
san - na in the high - est! Ho - san - na to your
mf
f
colla voce

King!
a tempo
dim.
p affret. poco a poco
And once a-gain the scene was chang'd, New earth there seem'd to be, I
pp
saw the ho-ly ci-ty Be-side the tide-less sea; The
light of God was on its streets, The gates were o-pen wide, And
cresc.

cantabile
all who would might en - - ter, And
f
no one was de - nied. No
dim.
p
need of moon or stars by night, Or
sun to shine by day, It
cresc.

affret.
was the hew Je - ru - - sa - lem That
p
allargando
would not pass a - way, It
cresc.
grandioso
rall.
was the new Je - ru - sa - lem That would not pass a -
f
rall.
a tempo
way. Je - ru - sa - lem! Je -
3
p a tempo

cresc.
ru - sa - lem! Sing, for the night is o'er! Ho -
cresc.
san - na in the high - est, Ho - san - na for ev - er -
mf
f
ad lib.
more! Ho - san - na in the high - est, Ho -
colla voce
san - na for ev - er - more!
ff

The Lord is my light

Text from
Psalm xxvii

Frances Allitsen

risoluto
Whom, then, shall I fear? Whom, then, shall I
risoluto
fear? The Lord is the strength of my life, The
cresc.
brillante
cresc.
Lord is the strength of my life, Of whom
f
f marcato
then, shall I be a - fraid?
Ped.

marcato e marziale
Though an host of men were laid against me,
marcato
sf
mp tranquillo
Yet shall not my heart be afraid;
mp tranquillo
sf
cresc.
ff
And tho' there 'rose up war against me,
cresc.
ff
Meno mosso
p dolce
rall. molto
Yet will I put my trust in Him.
p dolce
rall. molto

Andantino
espress.
For, in the time of trou - ble, He shall
p
molto tranquillo e sostenuto
Ped. * Ped. * Ped. * Ped. *
hide me in His tab - er - na - - cle,
Ped. * Ped. * Ped. * Ped. *
Yea, in the se - cret pla - ces of His dwell - ing
Ped. * Ped. * Ped. * Ped. * Ped. * Ped. *
shall He hide me, And
Ped. * Ped. * Ped. * Ped. *

marcato
ac - cel - er - an - do
set me up up - on a
cres - cen - do
rock of stone.
ff
sf
Brillante e con brio
Ped.
rall. molto
Tempo I
The Lord is my light and
my sal - va - tion, Whom, then, shall I fear? Whom, then, shall I
risoluto
Ped.

cresc.
fear? The Lord is the strength of my life, The Lord is the
lunga
strength of my life, Of whom, then, shall I be a-fraid? Of
f marcato
sf
lunga
molto maestoso
whom, then, shall I be a-fraid?
molto maestoso
colla voce
a tempo
sf
più vivo
sf
fff

One Sweetly Solemn Thought

Sacred Song

(Mezzo - Soprano or Baritone)

PHOEBE CARY

R. S. Ambrose

Andante
Voice
Piano
One sweet-ly sol - emn thought Comes to me o'er and o'er;

I am near - er home to - day Than I've ev - er been be -
fore. Near - er my Fa - ther's house, Where the
many - y man - sions be; cresc. Near - er the great white
throne, pp Near - - er the crys - tal sea;
pp

Near - er the bounds of life, Where we lay our bur - dens
down; Near - er leav - ing the cross,
Near - er gain - ing the crown. But ly - ing dark - ly be -
tween, Wind - ing a - down thro' the night,

Is the si - lent, un - known stream, That leads at last to the
light.
rall.
Fa - ther, be near when my feet Are
p
slip - ping o'er the brink, For it may be I am
near - er home, Near - er now than I think.

„Mein gläubiges Herze, frohlocke."

"My heart ever faithful, sing praises."

JOHANN SEBASTIAN BACH.

Andante con moto.
Piano.
p
mf
legato
Mein gläu - bi-ges Her - ze, froh - lo - cke, sing', scherze,
My heart ev-er faith - ful, Sing prais - es, be joy - ful,
dim.
p
mein gläu bi-ges Her - ze, froh -
My heart ev-er faith - ful, Sing
lo - cke, sing', scher-ze, froh - lo - cke, sing', scher - ze, dein Je - sus ist nah; mein
prais - es, be joy - ful, sing prais - es, be joy - ful, Thy Je - sus is near; My
gläu - bi-ges Her - ze, froh - lo - cke, sing', scher-ze, fro - lo - cke, sing', scher-ze, dein
heart ev-er faith-ful, Sing prais - es, be joy - ful, sing prais - es, be joy - ful, Thy

Je - sus ist nah!
Je - sus is near!
mf
dim.
Weg Jam - mer, weg Kla - gen, weg Jam - mer, weg Kla - gen, ich
A - way with com - plain - ing, a - way with com - plain - ing, Faith
p
will euch nur sa - gen, mein Je - sus ist da; weg Jam-mer, weg Kla-gen, ich
ev - er main-tain - ing, My Je - sus is here; A - way with com-plain-ing, Faith
poco cresc.
dim.
p
will euch nur sa - gen, mein Je - sus ist da, mein Je - sus ist da;
ev - er main-tain-ing, My Je - sus is here, my Je - sus is here;
mf
weg
A-
cresc.

Jam-mer,weg Kla-gen,weg Jam-mer,weg Kla-gen,ich will_euch nur sa-gen,mein
way_with com-plain-ing, a-way_with com-plain-ing, Faith ev-er main-tain-ing, My
p
Je-sus ist da! Mein gläu-bi-ges Her-ze, froh-lo-cke, sing', scher-ze,
Je-sus is here! My heart_ev-er faith-ful, Sing prais-es, be joy-ful,
mf
mein gläu-bi-ges Her-ze, froh-
My heart_ev-er faith-ful, Sing
dim.
p
lo-cke, sing', scher-ze, froh-lo-cke, sing scher-ze, dein Je-sus ist da, froh-
prais-es, be joy-ful, sing prais-es, be joy-ful, Thy Je-sus is here, Sing

lo-cke, sing', scherze, froh - lo - - cke, sing', scher - -
praises, be joy-ful, sing prais - - es, be joy - -
- - ze, mein gläu - bi-ges Her-ze, froh - lo - cke, sing', scher-ze, froh-
- - ful, My heart_ev-er faith-ful, Sing prais - es, be joy-ful, sing
dim.
p
lo - cke, sing', scher - ze, dein Je - sus ist da!
prais - es, be joy - ful, Thy Je - sus is here!
mf
cresc.
f

The Palms
Les Rameaux

English version by
Theodore T. Barker

Jean-Baptiste Faure
Edited by Carl Deis

Andante maestoso
Piano
f
rall.
a tempo
p
Ped.
Voice
1. :O'er all the way green palms and blos - soms gay
1. Sur nos che - mins les ra - meaux et les fleurs
Are strewn this day in fes - tal prep - a - ra - tion;
Sont ré - pan - dus dans ce grand jour de fê - te.
p e cresc.
ff

Where Je - sus comes to wipe our tears a - way,
Jé - sus s'a - van - ce, il vient sé - cher nos pleurs,
rall.
E'en now the throng to wel - come Him pre - pare;
Dé - jà la fou - le à l'ac - cla - mer s'ap - prête;
rall. ff
a tempo
Join all and sing, His name de - clare,
Peu - ples, chan - tez, chan - tez en choeur,
mf a tempo
f
Let ev - 'ry voice re - sound with ac - cla - ma - tion. Ho -
Que vo - tre voix à no - tre voix ré - pon - de. Ho -
3
p
cresc.
sf

san - - na! Praise to the Lord!
san - - na! Gloi - re au Sei-gneur!
ff
slargando
largo
Bless Him who com-eth to bring us sal - va - - -
Bé - ni ce-lui qui vient sau-ver le mon - - -
col canto
largo
ff
Tempo I°
tion!
de!
rall.
p
Ped.
Ped.
Ped.

2. His word goes forth, and peo-ple by its might
2. Il a par-lé, les peu-ples à sa voix
3. Sing and re-joice, O blest Je-ru-sa-lem,
3. Ré-jou-is-toi, Sain-te Jé-ru-sa-lem,
3
Once more re-gain free-dom from de-gra-da-tion.
Ont re-cou-vré leur li-ber-té per-du-e;
Of all thy sons sing the e-man-ci-pa-tion.
De tes en-fants chan-te la dé-li-vran-ce;
p e cresc.
ff
Hu-man-i-ty doth give to each his right,
L'hu-ma-ni-té don-ne à cha-cun ses droits,
Through bound-less love the Christ of Beth-le-hem
Par cha-ri-té le Dieu de Beth-lé-em

rall.
While those in dark - ness are re - stored to light.
Et la lu - miè - re est à cha - cun ren - due;
Brings faith and hope to thee for - ev - er - more.
A - vec la foi t'ap - por - te l'es - pé - rance!
cresc.
rall. ff
slargando
a tempo
Join all and sing, His name de-clare,
Peu - ples, chan - tez, chan - tez en chœur,
mf a tempo
Let ev - 'ry voice re - sound with ac - cla - ma - tion - Ho
Que vo - tre voix à no - tre voix ré - pon - de. Ho -
p
cresc.
sf
f

san - na! Praise to the Lord!
san - na! Gloi - re au Sei-gneur!
ff
slargando
Bless Him who com-eth to bring us sal - va - - -
Bé - ni ce-lui qui vient sau-ver le mon - - -
slargando
largo
largo
ff
Tempo I°
tion!
de!
1.
2.
Ped.
Ped.
Ped.
Ped.

I know that my Redeemer liveth

From the "Messiah"

G.F. Händel

Larghetto

Soprano
Ich weiss, dass mein Er = lö = ser le = bet,
I know that my Re = deem = er liv = eth,
und dass er mich einst er = weckt
and that he shall stand at the lat = =
cresc.
mez:

, er weckt , am lez = = ten Tag.
= = ter day up = on the earth;
Ich weiss dass mein Er = lö = ser le = bet und dass er mich einst er = weckt
I know that my Re = deemer liv = eth, and that he shall stand
, dass er mich er = weckt am lezten Tag , er =
at the lat = = ter day up = on the earth
weckt am lez = ten Tag. Ich weiss dass mein Er = lö = ser le = bet und dass
up = on the earth; I know that my Re = deem = er liv = eth, and that

er mich einst er = weckt am lez = ten Tag, er = weckt
he shall stand at the lat = = = ter day up = = on the earth
, am lez = ten Tag.
, up = on the earth;
tr
mf
tr
cresc:
f
tr
p
Wenn Ver = we = sung
And tho' worms de =
mir gleich drohet,
stroy this bo = dy,
wird dies mein Au = ge Gott doch
Yet in my flesh shall I see

seh'n, wird dies mein Au = ge Gott doch seh'n.
God, yet in my flesh shall I see God.
tr
f
Ich weiss dass mein Er = lö = ser le = bet, wenn Ver =
tr
I know that my Re = deem = er liv = eth, and tho'
p
we = sung mir gleich dro = het, wird dies mein Au = ge Gott doch
worms de = stroy this bo = dy, yet in my flesh shall I see
seh'n, wird dies mein Au = = = ge Gott doch seh'n, es wird Gott
God, yet in my flesh shall I see God, shall I see

seh'n. Ich weiss dass mein Er = lö = ser le = bet,
God, I know that my Re = deem = er liv = eth.
tr
tr
f
denn Christ ist er = stan = den von dem Tod, ein
For now is Christ ri = sen from the dead, the
p
Erst = = ling de = rer die schla = = = = fen, ein
first fruits of them that sleep, of
Erst = ling de = rer die schla = fen, die schla = = fen,
them that sleep, the first fruits of them that sleep,
f

denn Christ ist er = stan = den, denn Christ ist er =
For now is Christ ri = sen, for now is Christ
tr
p
stan = den von dem Tod,
ri = sen from the dead,
ein Erst = ling
the first
Adagio.
de = rer die schla = = fen
fruits of them that sleep.
tr
f
p
tr
cresc:
f
tr

Hosanna!

English version by
N. H. DOLE

Jules Granier

Maestoso (ma non lento)
Piano
ff
Ped.
Un poco più lento (ma poco)
p
A man is
Un homme est
ff
dead, he will a-rise a-gain, He will ap-pear, fear not, O Christian
mort, Il va re-naî-tre. Peu-ples chré-tiens, Il va pa-raî-

25000

cresc.
men! Shed not a tear! Lift up your
tre! Ne pleu-res plus, Lè - -ves les
cresc.
p rit. a tempo
eyes! What prom-ise shines___ in the bright Eastern skies!___
yeux! Les sé-ra-phins___ Il-lu-mi-nent les cieux.___
marcato il canto
rit.
p
a tempo
Un poco animato
Hear the Ser-a-phim sing-ing, In yon a-zure up-wing-ing!
Dans la sphère a-zu-ré-e C'est leur voix ins-pi-ré-e
marcata la melodia
cresc.
f
Hear them bless-ing the Lord, The Re-deem-er a-dored.___
Qui bé-nit le Sei-gneur, Jé-sus-Christ___ ré-demp-teur.___
cresc.
f
rit.

Maestoso (ma non lento)
mf
O Christ, Thy love o'er - whelm - eth me With ce - lest - ial
O Jésus, tu m'em - bra - ses De cé - les - tes ex -
ec - sta - sy! Thou art mine, O King di -
ta - ses! Je te vois, Ô di - vin
cresc.
vine! Ho - san - na! Ho - san - na! Ho -
roi! Ho - san - na! Ho - san - na! Ho -
f
allarg.
san - na! Praise be Thine! Ho - san - na! Praise be Thine!
san - na! gloire à toi! Ho - san - na! gloire à toi!
ff molto rit.
ff
f rall.

ff
Un poco più lento
p
Night, like_ a pall, seem'd to dis-pel the day, When God's dear
La som-bre nuit Voi-lait en-co- - -re Du fils de
pp
cresc.
Son pass'd from the world a - way, But now on high beams pur-est
Dieu La sainte au-ro - - -re, Mais le so-leil A res-plen-
cresc.
f
p
rit.
a tempo
light, Cre - a - tion bows___ o-verawed at the sight!___
di, Et l'u-ni- - vers___ Se prosterne é-blou-i.______
marcato il canto
dim.
p
rit.
a tempo
p

Un poco animato
p
By Archan - gels at - tend - - ed, And count-less le - gions
Au mi-lieu des pha - lan - - ges Des an - ges, des ar -
ben marcata la melodia
splen - did, Lo! the Sun soars a - bove, His face sub-lime with
chan - ges, Voy - ez-le s'a-van-çant Su - bli - me et tri - om -
cresc.
f
rit.
Maestoso (ma non lento)
love! O Christ, Thy love o'er-whelm - eth me
phant! O Jé - sus, tu m'em-bra - - - ses
With ce - lest - ial ec - - - sta - sy!
De cé - les - tes ex - ta - - - ses!
l.h.

cresc.
f
Thou___ art mine,___ O King di-vine!___ Ho-
Je___ te vois,___ Ô di-vin roi!___ Ho-
cresc.
f
cresc.
allarg.
san- - - na! Ho-san- - - na! Ho - san - na! Praise be
san- - - na! Ho-san- - - na! Ho - san - na! gloire à
f
allarg.
ff molto rit.
Thine!___ Ho - san - na! Praise be Thine!___
toi!___ Ho - san - na! gloire à toi!___
ff
f rall.
ff a tempo

I'm a Pilgrim

Mary S. B. Dana

Herbert Johnson

Andante con espressione
Voice
Piano
mp
p
I'm a
pil - grim, and I'm a stran - ger, I can tar - ry, I can tar - ry but a
night. Do not de - tain me, for I am go - ing, yea, go-ing

mf
Where the life is fair and bright. There the glo - ry is ev - er
mf
Ped.
shin - ing, Oh my long-ing heart, my long-ing heart is there. Here in this
coun-try so dark and drear-y, Too long I've wandered, sad and wea - ry.
rit.
a tempo
rit.
mf
Ped.
f
dim.
rit.
p

Poco maestoso
mf
There's the city, to which I journey, My Redeemer is my guide, my light.
Ped. Ped. Ped. Ped. simile
rit.
rit. dim.
mf a tempo
There is no sighing, Nor any dying,
f
Thou art my star, by day and by night. I'm a
p

Andante con espressione
pil - grim, and I'm a stran-ger, I can tar-ry, I can tar-ry but a night.— Do not de-
Ped.
rit. a tempo mf
tain me,— for I am go - ing, yea,go-ing Where the life is fair and bright,— There the
rit. a tempo
glo - ry— is ev-er shin-ing, Oh my long-ing heart, my long-ing heart is there.— Here in this
mf
dim. rit.
coun-try— so dark and drear-y,— Too long I've wan - dered, sad and wea - ry.
dim. rit. p

Open the Gates of the Temple

Words by
Fanny Crosby

Music by
Mrs. Joseph F. Knapp

Moderato
Voice
Piano
mf
Largo
mf
O - pen, O - pen,
ff Andante Maestoso
O - pen the gates of the
ff
tem - ple, O - pen the gates of the tem - ple,
rit.
a tempo
rit.
p a tempo

p Animato
O - pen the gates of the tem - ple. Strew palms on the Con-quer-or's way.
O - pen the gates of the tem - ple. One grand hal - le - lu - jah be heard.
O - pen your hearts O ye peo - ple, That
O - pen your hearts O the Sav - iour, Make
mf
Je - sus may en - ter to - day.
room for the cru - ci - fied Lord.
Hark! from the sick and the dy - ing, For - get - ting their couch - es of pain.
Tears and the an - guished of mid - night, Are lost in the splen - dor of day.

accel. e cresc.
a tempo
Voic - es, glad voic - es with rap - ture Are swell - ing, are
They_ who in sor - row once doubt - ed Are swell - ing, are
accel. e cresc.
rall.
swell - ing, are swell-ing a glad_ re - frain
swell - ing, are swell-ing a glad_ re - frain
mf accel. e cresc.
rall.
Voic - es, glad voic - es with rap - ture Are swell - ing a
They who in sor - row once doubt - ed Are swell - ing the
mf accel. e cresc.
sf rall.
1.
glad, a glad re - frain.
glad, a glad re - frain.
a tempo
rall.

2.
p
frain I know, I know, I
p
know, "I know that my Re-
deem - er liv - eth"
mf cresc.
Canst thou, my heart, lift up thy
p cresc. poco a poco

rall.
f
mf
f a tempo
voice thy voice and sing I know; I know, yes, I
rall.
f
pp
f Con passione
know that my Re - deem - er liv - eth, And be -
mf a tempo
cause He lives, and be - cause He lives, and be -
cresc.
ff
rall. e parlando
cause He lives, I too, I too, I too shall live.
ff slargando e pomposo
pp colla voce

Calvary

Word by HENRY VAUGHAN

(For Mezzo-Soprano or Baritone)

PAUL RODNEY

Maestoso
PIANO
f
dim.
mp
mf
The pil - grims throng thro' the
cit - y gates While the night is fall - ing fast;
They
go to watch on Cal - v'ry's hill Ere the twi - light hours are
p

mf
past; Though dark be the way, with eyes — of faith — They
mf
gaze on His Cross a - - bove; And, lo! from each heart — the
p espress.
p
shad - ows de-part, As they list to His words of love, as they
f cresc.
rall.
list to His words of love.
rit.
p rit.
6/4

Andante.
p con espress.
"Rest, rest to the wea - ry, Peace, peace to the soul; Though life may be
drear - y, Earth is not thy goal. O lay down thy bur - den,
O come un - to Me, I will not for - sake thee, I will not forsake thee, I will not for - sake thee, Though all else should flee."
p con espress.
f
p
mf con molto espress.
mf
f rall.
f

Giubiloso.
f
Far, far a-way, o'er the
dream — of years, — They hear the Voice of the King: —
"Where, O Grave, where is thy vic - - to-ry, And where, O Death, is — thy
rall.
sting?" —
f a tempo.
Cap - tive He leads them for ev - - er-more, — While

wea - ry pil - grims re - joice; For look - ing on high to the
cresc. f
Cross He bore, The faith - ful shall hear His Voice, the
f
rall.
rit.
faith - ful shall hear His Voice:
rall.
rit.
Andante.
p con espress.
"Rest, rest to the wea - ry, Peace, peace to the soul;
p con espress.

Though life may be drear - y, Earth is not thy goal. O lay down thy
bur - den, O come un - to Me, I will not for - sake thee,
mf con molto espress.
I will not for - sake thee, I will not for - sake thee, Though all else should
f rall.
flee, though all else should flee."
rit.

Ave Maria

Fr. Schubert

Lento
Voice
Piano
pp
1. A - - ve Ma-ri- - a! Maid - en mild, Ah! lis - ten to a maid - en's
2. A - - ve Ma-ri- - a! Un - de - fil'd! The flint - y couch where - on we're
3. A - - ve Ma-ri- - a! Stain - less styl'd! Each fiend of air or earth - ly

prayer; For Thou canst hear, though from the
sleep - - ing Shall seem with down of ei - der
es - - sence, From this their wont - ed haunt ex -
wild, 'Tis Thou, 'tis Thou canst save a -
pil'd, If Thou a - bove sweet watch art
il'd, Shall flee be - fore Thy ho - ly
mid des - pair. Safe
keep - - - ing. The
pres - - - ence! We
may we sleep un - til the mor - row, Though ban - ish'd, out - cast and re - vil'd. Oh
murk - y cav - ern's air so heav - y Shall breathe of balm if Thou hast smil'd; Then,
bow, be - neath our cares o'er - lad - en, Now to Thy guidance rec - on - cil'd; Then

Maid - en, see a maid - en's sor - row; Oh
Maid - en, hear a maid - en plead - ing, Oh
hear, oh Maid, a sim - ple maid - en, And
fp
Moth - er, hear a sup - pliant child!
Moth - er, hear a sup - pliant child!
for a fa - ther hear a child!
pp
A - ve Ma - ri - a!
A - ve Ma - ri - a!
A - ve Ma - ri - a!
dim.

727

Abide with me

H. F. Lyte

"Eventide"
W. H. Monk

(♩ = 92)
mf
1. A - bide with me: fast falls the e - ven - tide;
mf
p
The dark-ness deep-ens; Lord, with me a - bide: When oth-er help-ers
p
cresc.
p
fail, and comforts flee, Help of the help-less, O a - bide with me. A - men.
cresc.
p

2. *p* Swift to its close ebbs out life's little day;
Earth's joys grow dim, its glories pass away,
Change and decay in all around I see;
mf O Thou who changest not, (*p*) abide with me.

3. *f* I need Thy presence every passing hour;
cr. What but Thy grace can foil the tempter's power?
Who, like Thyself, my guide and stay can be?
f Through cloud and sunshine, Lord, (*p*) abide with me.

4. *f* I fear no foe, with Thee at hand to bless:
Ills have no weight, and tears no bitterness.
Where is death's sting? where, grave, thy victory?
I triumph still, if Thou abide with me.

5. *p* Hold Thou Thy Cross before my closing eyes:
cr. Shine through the gloom, and point me to the skies:
p Heaven's morning breaks and earth's vain shadows flee:
dim. In life, in death, O Lord, abide with me.

Come, my soul, thou must be waking

H. J. Buckoll
From the German
of F. R. L. Canitz

J. S. B. Hodges

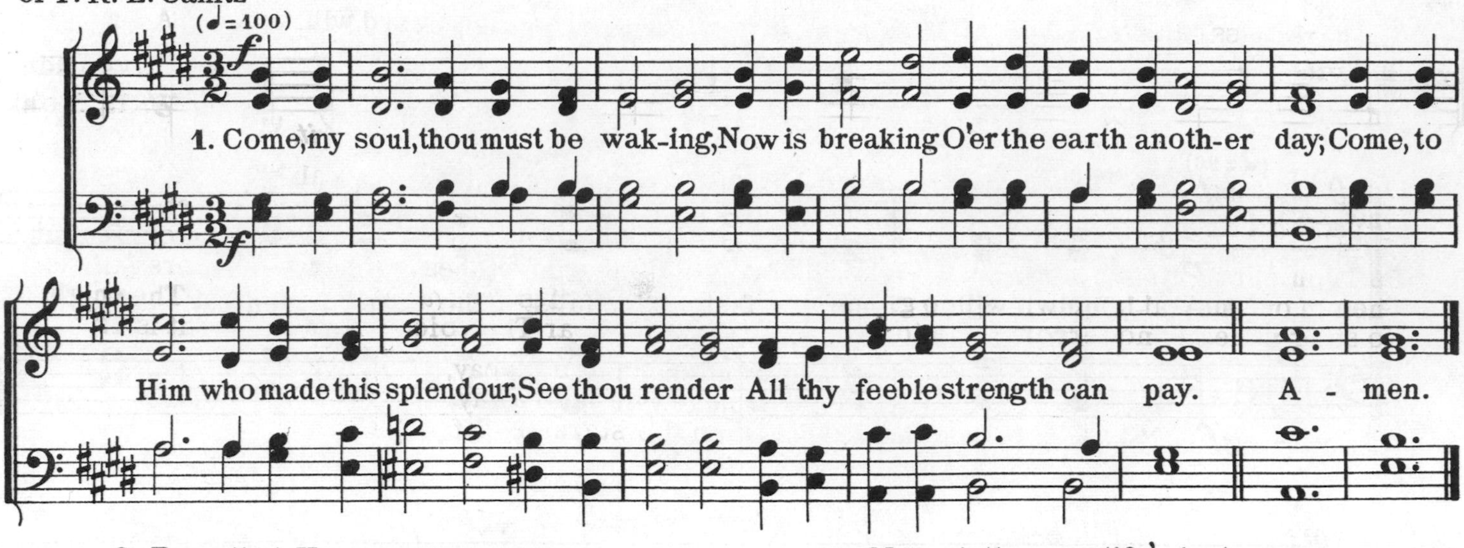
(♩=100)
f
1. Come, my soul, thou must be wak-ing, Now is breaking O'er the earth anoth-er day; Come, to
Him who made this splendour, See thou render All thy feeble strength can pay. A - men.

2. Pray that He may prosper ever
Each endeavor,
When thine aim is good and true:
But that He may ever thwart thee,
And convert thee,
When thou evil wouldst pursue.

3. Think that He thy ways beholdeth,
He unfoldeth
Every fault that lurks within:
He the hidden shame glossed over
Can discover,
And discern each deed of sin.

4. Mayest thou on life's last morrow,
Free from sorrow,
Pass away in slumber sweet:
And, released from death's dark sadness,
Rise in gladness,
That far brighter Sun to greet.

5. Only God's free gifts abuse not,
Light refuse not,
But His Spirit's voice obey;
Thou with Him shalt dwell, beholding
Light enfolding
All things in unclouded day.

The day is gently sinking to a close

C. Wordsworth

J. Barnby

(♩=108)
p
1. The day is gen - tly sink - ing to a close, Faint - er and
yet more faint the sun-light glows; O Bright-ness of Thy Fa-ther's glo - ry,
cresc.
Thou E - ter - nal Light of Light, be with us now; Where Thou art pres - ent,
f
p
pp

cresc.
dim.
rit.
dark-ness can-not be: Mid-night is glo-rious noon, O Lord, with Thee. A-men.
cresc.
dim.
rit.

2. *p* Our changeful lives are ebbing to an end:
Onward to darkness and to death we tend:
cr. O Conqueror of the grave, be Thou our guide,
f Be Thou our light *(dim.)* in death's dark eventide;
Then in our mortal hour will be no gloom,
No sting in death, no terror in the tomb.

3. *mf* Thou, Who in darkness walking didst appear
Upon the waves, and Thy disciples cheer,
Come, Lord, in lonesome days, when storms assail,
dim. And earthly hopes and human succors fail:
p When all is dark *(cr.)* may we behold Thee nigh,
And hear Thy voice: "Fear not, for it is I."

4. *p* The weary world is mouldering to decay,
Its glories wane, its pageants fade away;
cr. In that last sunset when the stars shall fall,
ff May we arise awakened by Thy call,
dim. With Thee, O Lord, forever to abide
cr. In that blest day which has no eventide.

A Mighty Fortress is Our God

Martin Luther, 1529

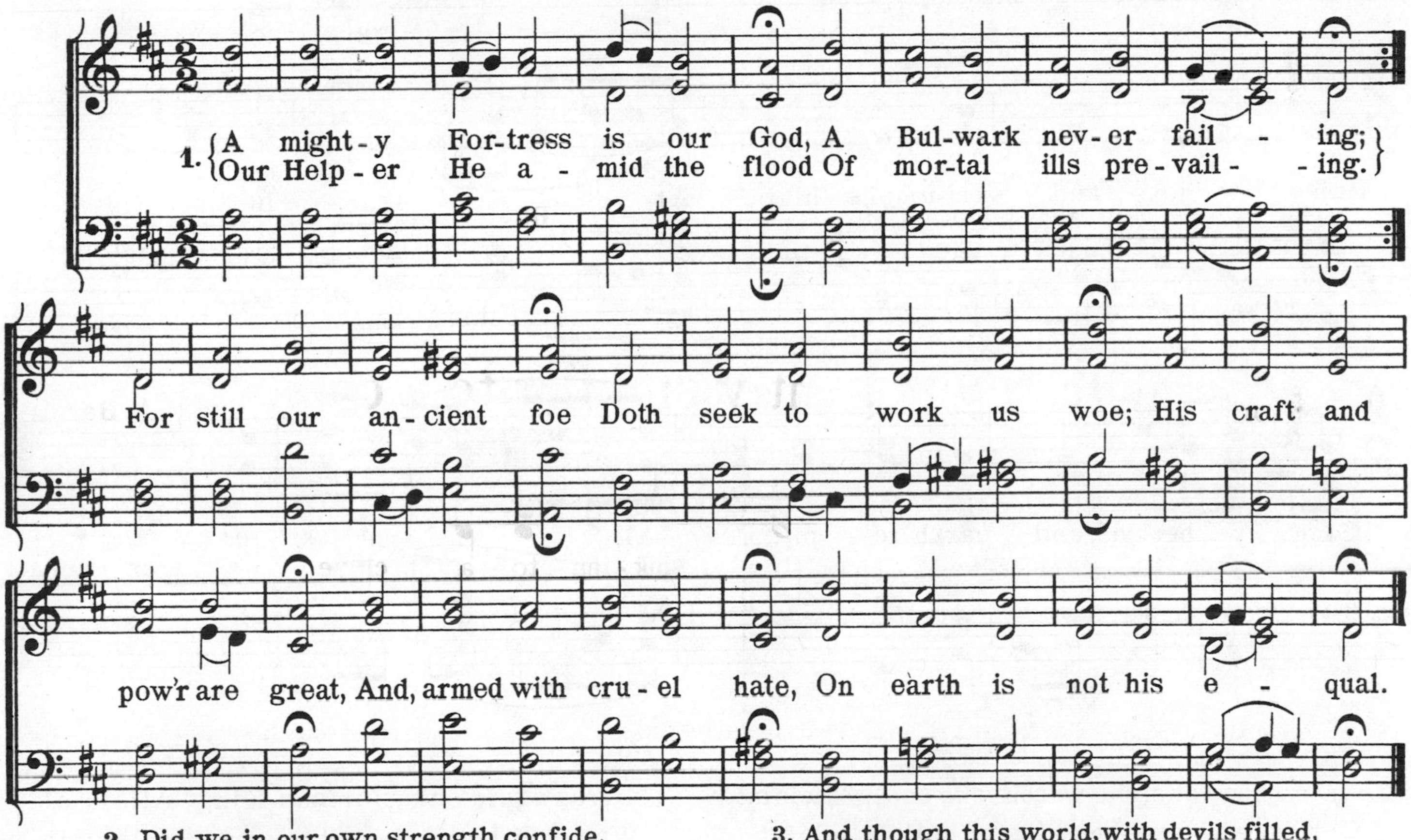

{Our Help-er He a - mid the flood Of mor-tal ills pre-vail - - ing.}
For still our an-cient foe Doth seek to work us woe; His craft and
pow'r are great, And, armed with cru - el hate, On earth is not his e - qual.

2. Did we in our own strength confide,
Our striving would be losing;
Were not the right man on our side,
The man of God's own choosing:
Dost ask who that may be?
Christ Jesus, it is He;
Lord Sabaoth His Name,
From age to age the same,
And He must win the battle.

3. And though this world, with devils filled,
Should threaten to undo us,
We will not fear, for God hath willed
His truth to triumph through us:
The prince of darkness grim,
We tremble not for him;
His rage we can endure,
For lo! his doom is sure,
One little word shall fell him.

4. That word above all earthly powers,
No thanks to them, abideth;
The Spirit and the gifts are ours
Through Him who with us sideth:
Let goods and kindred go,
This mortal life also;
The body they may kill:
God's truth abideth still,
His kingdom is for ever.

730

Christ, the Lord, Is Risen Today

Charles Wesley

Henry Carey

Christ, the Lord, is ris'n to - day, Al - le - lu - ia!
Sons of men and an - gels say, Al - le - lu - ia!
Raise your joys and tri-umphs high, Al - le - lu - ia!
Sing, ye heav'ns, and earth re - ply. Al - le - lu - ia!

2. Vain the stone, the watch, the seal, Alleluia!
Christ has burst the gates of hell. Alleluia!
Death in vain forbids His rise, Alleluia!
Christ has opened Paradise. Alleluia!

3. Lives again our glorious King, Alleluia!
Where, O death, is now thy sting? Alleluia!
Once He died our souls to save, Alleluia!
Where thy victory, O grave? Alleluia!

4. Soar we now where Christ has led, Alleluia!
Following our exalted Head. Alleluia!
Made like Him, like Him we rise, Alleluia!
Ours the cross, the grave, the skies. Alleluia!

25000

Jesu, Lover of my Soul

Charles Wesley

"Hollingside"
J. B. Dykes

(♩= 80)
p
cresc.
mf
dim.
1. Je - su, Lov - er of my soul, Let me to Thy bo - som fly,
While the near - er wa - ters roll, While the tem - pest still is high;
Hide me, O my Sav - iour, hide, Till the storm of life be past;
Safe in - to the ha - ven guide, Oh, re - ceive my soul at last. A - men.

2. *mp* Other refuge have I none,
Hangs my helpless soul on Thee;
Leave, ah! leave me not alone,
Still support and comfort me:
cr. All my trust on Thee is stayed;
All my help from Thee I bring;
p Cover my defenseless head
With the shadow of Thy wing.

3. *mf* Plenteous grace with Thee is found,
Grace to cleanse from every sin;
Let the healing streams abound,
Make and keep me pure within:
cr. Thou of life the fountain art,
Freely let me take of Thee;
f Spring Thou up within my heart,
Rise to all eternity.

Nearer, my God, to Thee

Sarah Adams

"Bethany"
Lowell Mason

(𝅗𝅥 = 45)
mf
p
1. Near-er, my God, to Thee, Near-er to Thee,_ E'en tho' it be a cross
cresc.
That_ rais-eth me;_ Still all my song shall be, Near-er, my
dim.
God, to Thee, Near-er, my God, to Thee, Near-er to Thee. A-men.

2. *p* Though like a wanderer,
Weary and lone,
Darkness comes over me,
My rest a stone;
cr. Yet in my dreams I'd be
Nearer, my God, to Thee,
dim. Nearer to Thee.

3. *mf* There let my way appear
Steps unto heaven;
All that Thou sendest me
In mercy given;
Angels to beckon me
cr. Nearer, my God, to Thee,
dim. Nearer to Thee.

4. *mf* Then with my waking thoughts
Bright with Thy praise,
Out of my stony griefs,
Altars I'll raise;
So by my woes to be
cr. Nearer, my God, to Thee,
dim. Nearer to Thee.

5. *f* Or if on joyful wing
Cleaving the sky,
Sun, moon and stars forgot,
Upward I fly,
Still all my song shall be
Nearer, my God, to Thee,
dim. Nearer to Thee.

733

Stand Up for Jesus

George Duffield — George J. Webb

Stand up, stand up for Je - sus, Ye sol-diers of the cross; Lift
high His roy - al ban - ner, It must not suf - fer loss; From
vic - t'ry un - to vic - t'ry, His ar - my shall He lead, — Till
ev - 'ry foe is van-quish'd, And Christ is Lord in - deed. A - men.

2. Stand up, stand up for Jesus,
The trumpet call obey;
Forth to the mighty conflict,
In this His glorious day.
Ye that are men, now serve Him,
Against unnumber'd foes;
Let courage rise with danger,
And strength to strength oppose.

3. Stand up, stand up for Jesus,
Stand in His strength alone;
The arm of flesh will fail you,
Ye dare not trust your own;
Put on the gospel armor,
Each piece put on with pray'r;
Where duty calls, or danger,
Be never wanting there.

4. Stand up, stand up for Jesus,
The strife will not be long;
This day the noise of battle,
The next the victor's song;
To him that overcometh,
A crown of life shall be;
He with the King of glory
Shall reign eternally.

Onward, Christian Soldiers

S. Baring-Gould | "St. Gertrude" A. S. Sullivan

(♩ = 108)
f
1. Onward, Christian soldiers, Marching as to war, With the cross of Jesus
Going on before! Christ, the royal Master, Leads against the foe;
mf
Forward into battle, See, His banners go. Onward, Christian soldiers,
ff
Marching as to war, With the cross of Jesus Going on before! Amen.

2. *f* At the sign of triumph
 Satan's host doth flee;
On, then, Christian soldiers,
 On to victory!
Hell's foundations quiver
 At the shout of praise;
Brothers, lift your voices,
 Loud your anthems raise!
ff Onward, etc.

3. *f* Like a mighty army
 Moves the Church of God;
Brothers, we are treading
 Where the saints have trod;
We are not divided,
 All one Body we,
One in hope and doctrine,
 One in charity.
ff Onward, etc.

4. *mf* Crowns and thrones may perish,
 Kingdoms rise and wane,
f But the Church of Jesus
 Constant will remain;
Gates of hell can never
 'Gainst that Church prevail;
We have Christ's own promise,
 And that cannot fail.
ff Onward, etc.

5. *f* Onward, then, ye people!
 Join our happy throng!
Blend with ours your voices
 In the triumph song!
Glory, laud and honor
 Unto Christ the King;
This through countless ages
 Men and angels sing.
ff Onward, etc.

A. M. Toplady

Rock of Ages

"Toplady"
T. Hastings

(♩= 90)
mf
dim.
1. Rock of a - ges, cleft for me, Let me hide my-self in Thee; Let the
wa - ter and the blood From Thy side, a heal - ing flood, Be of
cresc.
sin the dou - ble cure, Save from wrath and make me pure. A - men.

2. *p* Should my tears for ever flow,
Should my zeal no languor know,
All for sin could not atone,
cr. Thou must save, and Thou alone;
In my hand no price I bring,
Simply to Thy cross I cling.

3. *pp* While I draw this fleeting breath,
When mine eyelids close in death,
cr. When I rise to worlds unknown,
And behold Thee on Thy throne:
mf Rock of ages, cleft for me,
p Let me hide myself in Thee.

G. W. Doane

Softly now the light of day

"Weber"
C. M. von Weber

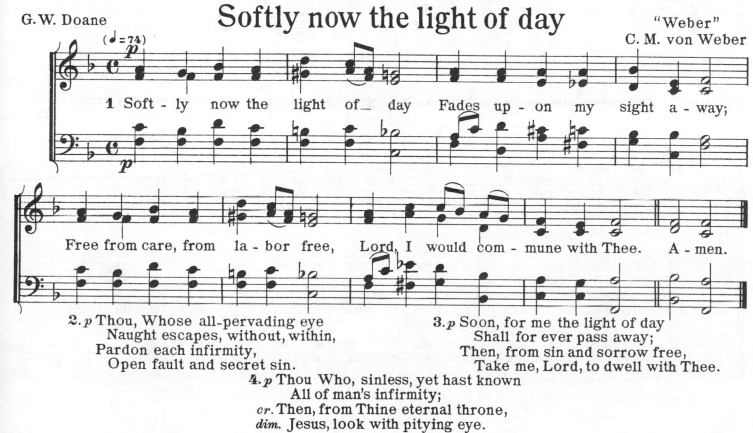

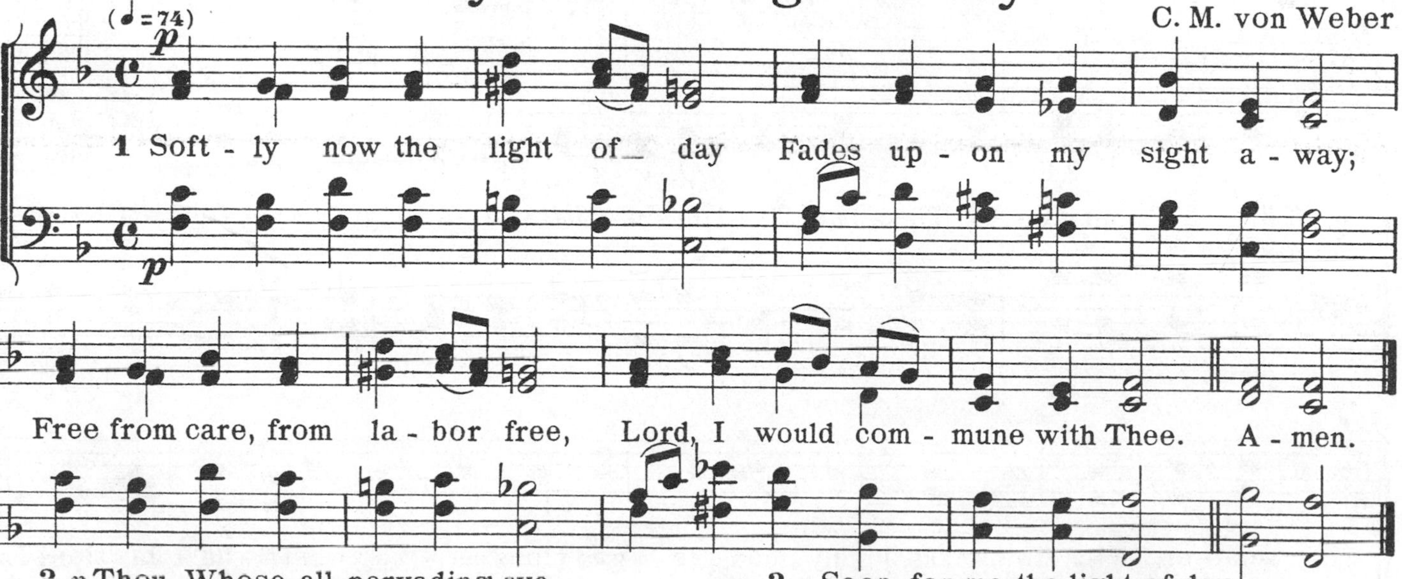
(♩= 74)
p
1 Soft - ly now the light of_ day Fades up - on my sight a - way;
Free from care, from la - bor free, Lord, I would com - mune with Thee. A - men.

2. *p* Thou, Whose all-pervading eye
Naught escapes, without, within,
Pardon each infirmity,
Open fault and secret sin.

3. *p* Soon, for me the light of day
Shall for ever pass away;
Then, from sin and sorrow free,
Take me, Lord, to dwell with Thee.

4. *p* Thou Who, sinless, yet hast known
All of man's infirmity;
cr. Then, from Thine eternal throne,
dim. Jesus, look with pitying eye.

736

Prayer Of Thanksgiving

We Gather Together

English version by Dr. Th. Baker | Ancient Folk-song of the Netherlands

1. We gath-er to-geth-er to ask the Lord's bless-ing, He chast-ens and hast ens His will to make known; The wick-ed op-press-ing, cease them from dis-tress-ing, Sing prais-es to His name,— He for-gets not His own.
2. Be-side us to guide us, our God with us join-ing, Or-dain-ing, main-tain-ing His King-dom di-vine. So from the be-gin-ning the fight— we were win-ning, Thou Lord, wast at our side,— The— glo-ry be Thine.
3. We all do ex-tol Thee, Thou Lead-er in bat-tle, And pray that Thou still our De-fend-er wilt be. Let Thy con-gre-ga-tions es-cape— tri-bu-la-tion; Thy

name be ev-er praised, O— Lord, make us free! Lord make us free!

Fairest Lord Jesus, Ruler of All Nature

Crusaders' Hymn

Anonymous. From 12th Century

German Air

1. Fair - est Lord Je - sus, Ru - ler of all na - ture, O, Thou of
2. Fair are the mead - ows, Fair - er still the wood - lands, Rob'd in the
3. Fair is the sun - shine, Fair - er still the moon - light, And all the
God and — man the Son, Thee will I cher - ish,
bloom - ing — garb of spring; Je - sus is fair - er,
twink - ling — star - ry host; Je - sus shines bright - er,
Thee will I hon - or, Thou, my soul's glo - ry, joy and crown.
Je - sus is pur - er, Who makes the woe - ful heart to sing.
Je - sus shines pur - er, Than all the an - gels heav'n can boast.

Blest Be the Tie That Binds

John Fawcett | Hans G. Nageli

2. Be-fore— our Fa-ther's throne, We pour— our ar-dent pray'rs;
3. We share— our mu-tual woes, Our mu-tual bur-dens bear;
4. When we— a-sun-der part, It gives— us in-ward pain;
The fel-low-ship— of kin-dred minds— Is like— to that— a-bove.
Our fears, our hopes, our aims— are one,— Our com-forts and— our cares.
And oft-en for— each oth-er flows— The sym-pa-thiz-ing tear.
But we— shall still— be joined in heart,— And hope— to meet— a-gain.

Jesus Calls Us

Cecil F. Alexander | W. H. Jude

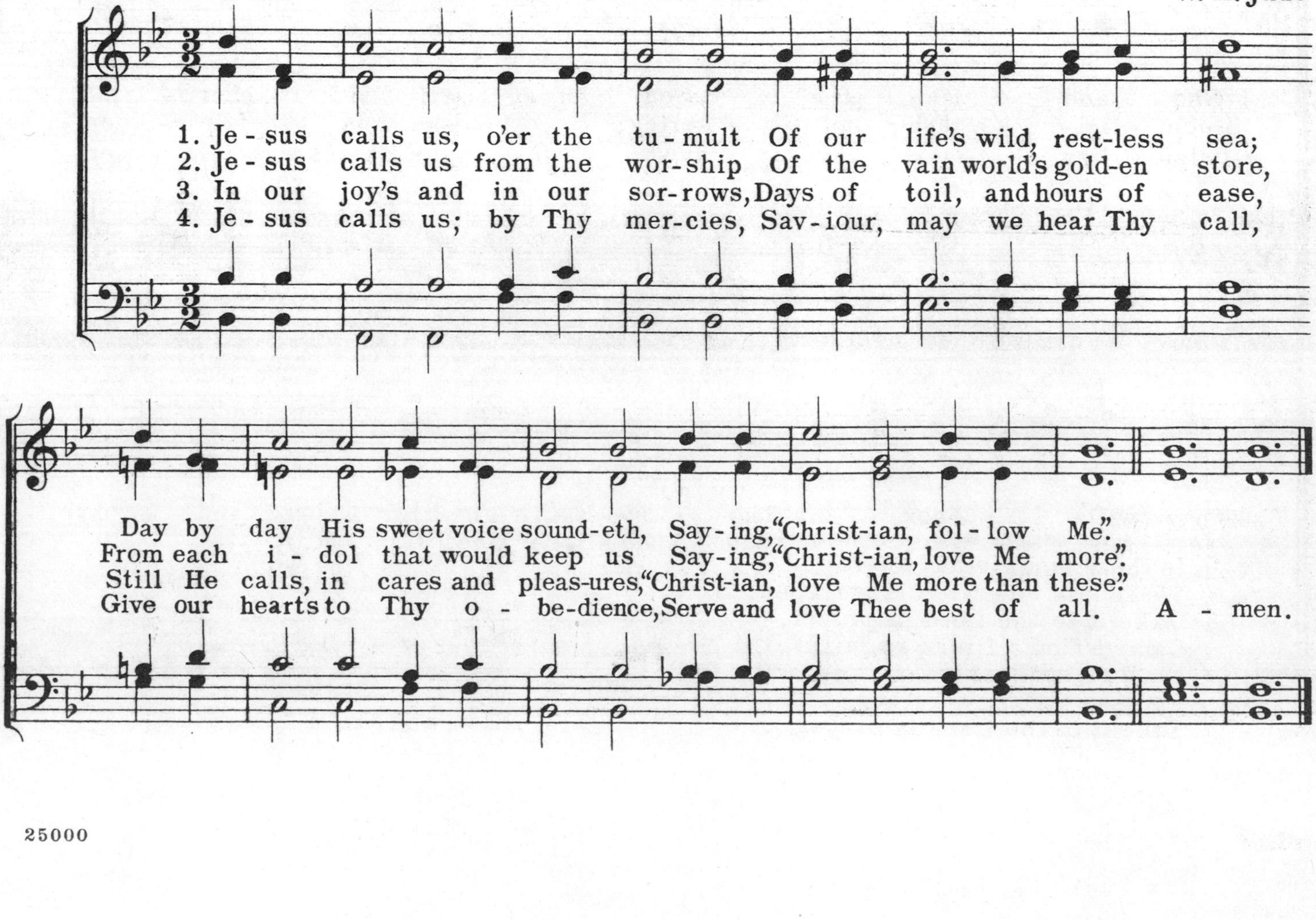

1. Je-sus calls us, o'er the tu-mult Of our life's wild, rest-less sea;
2. Je-sus calls us from the wor-ship Of the vain world's gold-en store,
3. In our joy's and in our sor-rows, Days of toil, and hours of ease,
4. Je-sus calls us; by Thy mer-cies, Sav-iour, may we hear Thy call,
Day by day His sweet voice sound-eth, Say-ing, "Christ-ian, fol-low Me."
From each i-dol that would keep us Say-ing, "Christ-ian, love Me more."
Still He calls, in cares and pleas-ures, "Christ-ian, love Me more than these."
Give our hearts to Thy o-be-dience, Serve and love Thee best of all. A-men.

739

What a Friend We Have in Jesus

Joseph Scriven — Charles C. Converse

What a Friend we have in Je - sus, All our sins and griefs to bear!
What a priv - i - lege to car - ry Ev - 'ry-thing to God in prayer!
O what peace we oft - en for - feit, O what need-less pain we bear,
All be-cause we do not car - ry Ev - 'ry-thing to God in prayer!

2. Have we trials and temptations?
Is there trouble anywhere?
We should never be discouraged,
Take it to the Lord in prayer.
Can we find a friend so faithful
Who will all our sorrows share?
Jesus knows our ev'ry weakness,
Take it to the Lord in prayer.

3. Are we weak and heavy-laden,
Cumbered with a load of care?
Precious Saviour, still our Refuge,
Take it to the Lord in prayer.
Do thy friends despise, forsake thee?
Take it to the Lord in prayer;
In His arms He'll take and shield thee,
Thou wilt find a solace there.

Praise God, From Whom All Blessings Flow

Doxology

L. Bourgeois

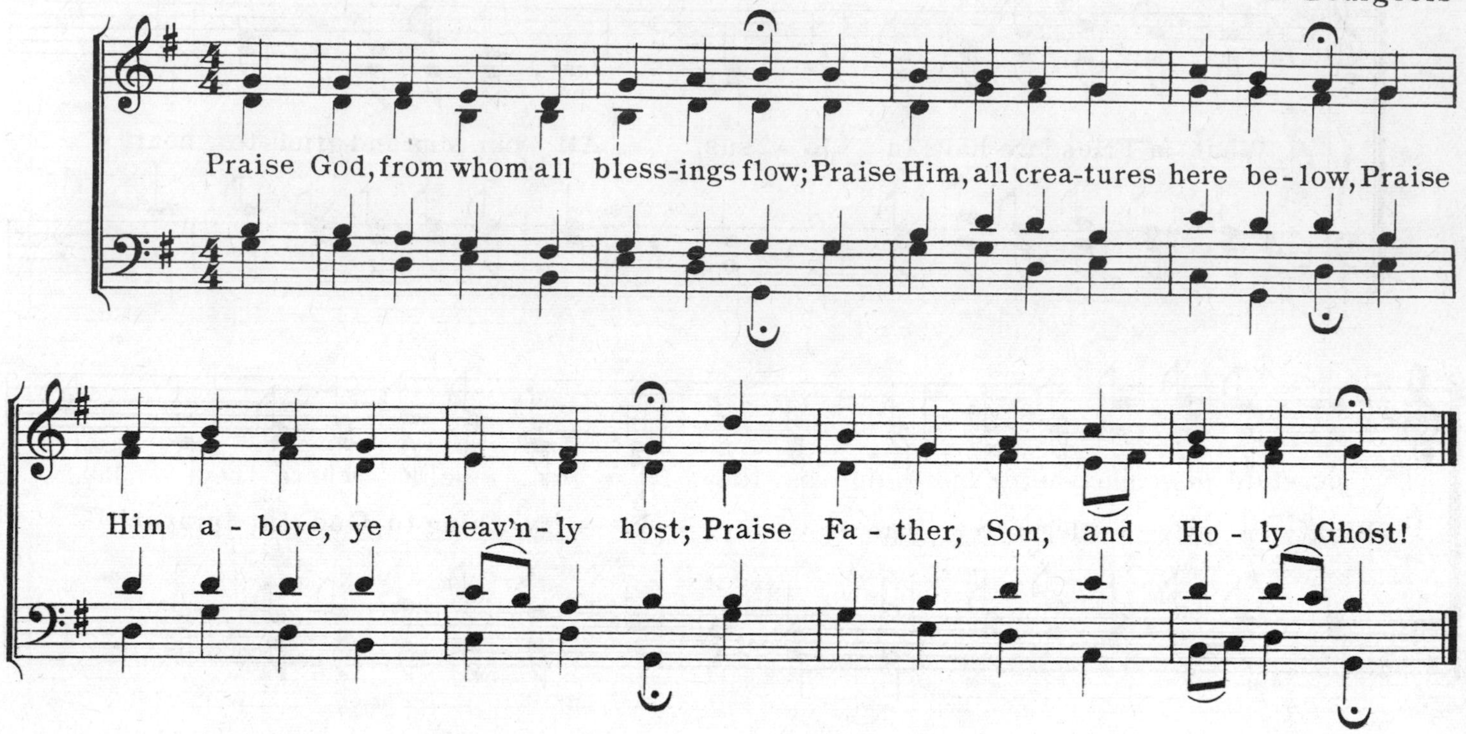
Praise God, from whom all bless-ings flow; Praise Him, all crea-tures here be-low, Praise
Him a-bove, ye heav'n-ly host; Praise Fa-ther, Son, and Ho-ly Ghost!

Now The Day Is Over

Sabine Baring-Gould

Joseph Barnby

1. Now the Day is o-ver, Night is draw-ing nigh;
2. Je-sus, give the wea-ry Calm and sweet re-pose,
3. When the morn-ing wak-ens, Then may we a-rise
Shad-ows of the ev'-ning Steal a-cross the sky.
With Thy tend-'rest bless-ing, May our eye-lids close.
Pure and fresh and sin-less In Thy ho-ly eyes.

The First Noël

Words traditional

Old English tune
harmonized by Sir John Stainer

p
1. The— first— No - el the— an - gels did say Was to
p
cer-tain poor shep-herds in fields as they lay; In— fields— where they lay—
keep-ing their sheep On a cold win-ter's night— that was— so deep.
Chorus
f
No - el,— No - el, No - el, No - el, Born is the King— of Is - ra - el.
f

2. They looked up and saw a Star
Shining in the East, beyond them far,
And to the earth it gave great light,
And so it continued both day and night.
Chorus

3. This star drew nigh to the northwest,
O'er Bethlehem it took its rest.
And there it did both stop and stay,
Right over the place where Jesus lay.
Chorus

4. Then enter'd in there wise men three,
Full rev'rently upon their knee,
And offer'd there in His presence,
Their gold and myrth and frankincense.
Chorus

Hark! the herald angels sing

Charles Wesley | Felix Mendelssohn-Bartholdy

Hark! the her - ald an-gels sing_ Glo - ry to the new-born King; Peace on earth and
mer - cy mild, God and sin-ners re-con-ciled! Joy-ful all ye na-tions, rise,_ Join the tri-umph
of the skies,_ With th'an-gel - ic host pro-claim Christ is_born in Beth - le - hem.
Refrain
Hark! the her - ald an - gels sing Glo - ry_ to the new-born King.

2. Christ, by highest heav'n adored;
Christ, the everlasting Lord;
Come, Desire of Nations, come,
Fix in us Thy humble home.
Veiled in flesh the God-head see;
Hail th'Incarnate Deity,
Pleased as Man with man to dwell;
Jesus, our Immanuel!
Refrain

3. Mild He lays His glory by,
Born that man no more may die;
Born to raise the sons of earth,
Born to give them second birth.
Ris'n with healing in His wings,
Light and life to all He brings,
Hail, the Son of Righteousness!
Hail, the heav'n-born Prince of Peace!
Refrain

743

It came upon a midnight clear

Edmund H. Sears (1846) Richard S. Willis (1850)

1. It came up-on_ a mid-night clear, That glo-rious song_of old.__
2. Still though the clo-ven skies they come, With peace-ful wings un-furled;_
From an-gels bend-ing near the earth, To touch their harps of gold:__
And still their heav'n-ly mu-sic floats, O'er all the wea-ry world:_
Peace on the earth, good-will to men, From heav'n's all gra-cious King;_
A-bove its sad_ and low-ly plains They bend_ on hov-'ring wing._
The world in sol-emn still-ness lay To hear the an-gels sing._
And ev-er o'er_ its Bab-el sounds The bless-ed an-gels sing._

Jingle Bells

J. Pierpont

With humor

mf
Dash-ing thro' the snow in a one horse o-pen sleigh
O'er the fields we go laugh-ing all the way.
Bells on bob-tail ring mak-ing spir-its bright What
fun it is to ride and sing a sleigh-ing song to-night.

Jin-gle bells, jin-gle bells, jin-gle all the way.
Oh what fun it is to ride in a one horse o-pen sleigh.
Jin-gle bells, jin-gle bells, jin-gle all the way
Oh what fun it is to ride in a one horse o-pen sleigh.
8
8

Joy to the world!

Isaac Watts (1719)

Arr. from George F. Handel (1742)
by Lowell Mason (1830)

♩= 88
1. Joy to the world! the Lord is come: Let earth re -
ceive her King, Let ev - 'ry_ heart_ pre - pare_ Him_
room,_ And heav'n and na - ture_ sing, And_ heav'n and na - ture_
And heav'n and na - ture sing,
sing, And_ heav'n,_ and heav'n_ and na - ture sing.
And heav'n
heav'n and na - ture sing,

2. Joy to the world! the Saviour reigns;
Let men their songs employ,
While fields and floods, rocks, hills and plains
Repeat the sounding joy.

3. He rules the world with truth and grace,
And makes the nations prove
The glories of His righteousness,
The wonders of His love.

O come, all ye faithful

From the Latin
by F. Oakeley

"Adeste Fideles"
J. Reading

(♩=112)
1. f O come, all ye faith - ful, Joy - ful and tri - um - phant, O come ye, O come ye to Beth - le - hem;
2. f God of God, Light of Light, p Lo! He ab - hors not the Vir - gin's womb;
3. f Sing, choirs of an - gels, Sing in ex - ul - ta - tion, Sing, all ye ci - ti - zens of heav'n a - bove:
4. f Yea, Lord, we greet Thee, Born this hap - py morn - ing, Je - sus, to Thee be glo - ry giv'n;
Come and be - hold Him born the King of an - gels;
Ver - y God, be - got - ten, not cre - at - ed;
Glo - ry to God in the high - est;
Word of the Fa - ther, now in flesh ap - pear - ing;
After each verse
p
cresc.
O come, let us a - dore Him, O come, let us a - dore Him,
f
O come, let us a - dore Him, Christ, the Lord. A - men.
cresc.
f

O holy night!
Cantique de Nöel

M. Cappeau de Roquemaure
Translated by John S. Dwight

Adolphe Adam

Slowly and majestically
mf
1. O holy night! the stars are brightly shining, It is the night of the dear Saviour's birth; Long lay the world in sin and error pining, Till He ap-
2. Led by the light of faith serenely beaming, With glowing hearts by His cradle we stand; So led by light of a star sweetly gleaming, Here came the
3. Truly He taught us to love one another; His law is love, and His gospel is peace; Chains shall He break, for the slave is our brother, And in His

p
peared and the soul felt its worth. A thrill of hope the
wise men from O - ri - ent land. The King of kings lay
name all op-pres - sion shall cease. Sweet hymns of joy in
pp
wea - ry soul re-joic - es, For yon - der breaks a new and glo-rious morn;—
thus in low - ly man - ger, In all our tri - als born to be our friend;
grate-ful cho-rus raise we, Let all with - in us praise His ho - ly name;—
1st time through refrain is sung by solo voice, 2nd time, four part.
f
Fall on your knees, Oh,— hear— the an - gel voi - ces! O
He knows our need, To our weak - ness is no stran - ger. Be-
Christ is the Lord, Oh,— praise— His name for - ev - er! His
f
f

night — di - vine, — O night — when Christ was born! O
hold — your King, — be - fore — Him low - ly bend! Be -
pow'r — and glo - - ry ev - er-more pro-claim! His
1.
night, — O ho - ly night, O night di - vine!
hold — your King, — be - fore Him low - ly bend!
pow'r — and glo - ry ev - er-more pro-claim!
2.
D.S. 𝄋
night, O ho - - ly — night, O night di - vine!
hold your King, — be - fore Him low - ly bend!
pow'r and glo - - ry — ev - er - more pro - claim!
D.S. 𝄋

From the Blue Book of Favorite Songs, published by Hall and McCreary, Chicago. Used by permission.

O Little Town of Bethlehem

Phillips Brooks, 1868 | Lewis H. Redner, 1868

mf
1. O lit-tle town of Beth-le-hem, How still we_ see thee lie, A-
bove thy deep and dream-less sleep The si-lent_ stars go by; Yet
in thy dark streets shin-eth The ev-er last-ing light, The
hopes and fears of all the years, Are met in thee to-night.

2. For Christ is born of Mary,
And gathered all above,
While mortals sleep, the angels keep
Their watch of wond'ring love.
O morning stars, together
Proclaim the holy birth
And praises sing to God, the King,
And peace to men on earth.

3. How silently, how silently,
The wond'rous gift is given;
So God imparts to human hearts
The blessings of His heaven.
No ear may hear His coming,
But in this world of sin,
Where meek souls will receive Him still,
The dear Christ enters in.

O Tannenbaum

From the German

mf
1. O Tan-nen-baum, O Tan-nen-baum! Your leaves are faith-ful ev-er!
2. O Tan-nen-baum, O Tan-nen-baum! You are the tree most lov-ed;
mp
Not on-ly, green when sum-mer glows, But in the win-ter when it snows.
How oft you've giv-en me de-light When Christ-mas fires were burn-ing bright!
mf
O Tan-nen-baum, O Tan-nen-baum! Your leaves are faith-ful ev-er.
O Tan-nen-baum, O Tan-nen-baum! You are the tree most lov-ed.

Note: "Tannenbaum" is the German word for *fir tree.*

Silent Night

Stille Nacht

Joseph Möhr

Franz Gruber, 1818

pp
1. Si - lent night, Ho - ly night! All is calm, all is bright,
pp
'Round yon Vir - gin Moth - er and Child, Ho - ly In - fant so ten - der and mild,
Sleep in heav - en - ly peace__ Sleep__ in heav - en - ly peace!__

2. Silent night, Holy night!
Shepherds quake at the sight!
Glories stream from heaven afar,
Heav'nly hosts sing Alleluia;
Christ, the Saviour, is born!
Christ, the Saviour, is born!

Silent night, Holy night!
Child of Heaven, O how bright
Thou didst smile when Thou wast born!
Blessed be that happy morn,
Full of heavenly joy,
Full of heavenly joy.

Australia

Advance, Australia Fair

(about 1885)

Words and Music by
P. D. McCormick
(1834-1916)

Maestoso
Voice
Piano
f
1. Aus - tra - lia's sons, let us re - joice, For we are young and free; We've gold - en soil and wealth for toil, Our home is girt by sea; Our land a - bounds in
2. Should for - eign foe e'er sight our coast, Or dare a foot to land, We'll rouse to arms like sires of yore To guard our na - tive strand; Brit - an - nia then shall
mf

na - ture's gifts, Of beau - ty rich and rare; In
sure - ly know, Tho' o - ceans roll be - tween, Her
f
p cresc.
his - t'ry's page, let ev - 'ry stage, Ad - vance, Aus - tra - lia fair.
sons in fair Aus - tra - lia's land Still keep her name se - rene. In
f
p cresc.
ff
D.C.
joy - ful strains then let us sing: Ad - vance, Aus - tra - lia fair.
ff

Austrian National Anthem

Paula Preradovic

Wolfgang Amadeus Mozart

1. Land der Ber - ge,_ Land am Stro - me, Land der Äk - ker,_ Land der
2. Heiss um - feh - det,_ wild um - strit - ten, liegst dem Erd - teil_ du in -
3. Mu - tig in die_ neu - en Zei - ten, frei und gläu - big_ sieh uns
Do - me, Land der Häm - mer, zu - kunfts-reich! Hei - mat bist_ du
mit - ten ei - nem star - ken Her - zen gleich. Hast seit frü - hen
schreiten, ar - beits-froh und hoff - nungs-reich. Ei - nig lass_ in
gros - ser_ Söh - ne, Volk, be - gna - det für das_ Schö - ne, viel - ge -
Ah - nen - ta - gen ho - her Sen - dung Last ge - tra - gen, viel - ge -
Brü - der - chö - ren Va - ter - land,_ dir Treu - e_ schwören, viel - ge -
rüh - tes Ö - ster - reich. Viel - ge - rühm - tes_ Ö - ster - reich.
prüf - tes Ö - ster - reich. Viel - ge - prüf - tes_ Ö - ster - reich.
lieb - tes Ö - ster - reich. Viel - ge - lieb - tes_ Ö - ster - reich.
f
p
f
ff

Belgium

The Brabançonne*

(1830)

Charles Rogier
(1800-1885)
English version by Lorraine Noel Finley

François van Campenhout
(1779-1848)

Allegro marziale
Voice
Piano
f
At last the Bel - gian_ res - ur - rec - tion Af - ter
A - près des siè - cles_ d'es - cla - va - ge Le_
†Juicht! Bel - gen, juicht! in_ vreug - devol'_ ak - koor-den Van Has-
long years of slav - er - y came;
Bel - ge sor-tant du tom-beau,
pen - gouw tot aan het Vlaamsche strand,
Cour - age re-stored to them pro-
A re - con-quis par son cou-
Van Noord tot Zuid, langs Maas en
tec - tion Of their rights, their flag and of their name.
ra - ge Son_ nom, ses droits et son dra - peau.
Schelde - boor-den, Juicht, Bel - gen, juicht door gansch het Vader - land!
mf
Then your
Et ta
Een man-

"The Brabançonne" means "The song of the people of Brabant." Brabant is the province of Belgium surrounding Brussels. Its citizens were the most active in demanding that Belgium be independent from Holland, which was accomplished by a brief revolution in 1830. The present official words were written in 1860, the earlier version by Janneval, having been too narrowly limited to political events of 1830.

†Official Flemish text. By Belgian law, public documents and notices, money, postage stamps, etc. are always printed in *both* Flemish and French.

hand, bold in its re - li - - ance, Proud Bel - gians, strong henceforth in
main sou - ve-raine et fiè - - re, Peu - ple dé - sor - mais in - domp-
lÿk-volk moet manlÿk dur - ven zin - - gen Terwÿl zÿn hart van eedle fier - heid
might, Up - on your flag in - scribed with de -
té, Gra - va sur ta vieil - le ban -
beeft; Nooit zal men ons een morzel gronds ont
f
fi - - ance: For* King, for Lib - er - ty and Right, Up - on your
niè - - re Le Roi, la loi, la li - ber - té! Gra - va
wring - - en Zoolang een, Belg, 't zy Waal of Vlaming leeft. Nooit zal men
3

*King Leopold III was born on Nov. 3, 1901 and came to the throne on Feb. 23, 1934 following the tragic death of his father, King Albert, in a mountain-climbing accident. When Belgium was brutally invaded in May 1940, King Leopold III personally led the heroic resistance of his people. He has been a prisoner of war since Belgium was forced to yield to overwhelming numbers.

flag in - scribed with de - fi - - - ance: For
sur ta vieil - le ban - niè - - - re Le
ons een morzel gronds ont wring - - - en Zoolang
King, for Lib - er - ty and Right, For King, for Lib - er - ty and
Roi, la loi, la li - ber - té, Le Roi, la loi, la li - ber -
een Belg,'t zy Waal of Vlaming leeft Zoolang een Belg,'t zy Waal of Vlaming
Right, For King, for Lib - er - ty and Right.
té, Le Roi, la loi, la li - ber - té!
leeft Zoolang een Belg 't zy Waal of Vlaming leeft.
sf

Danish National Anthem

H. E. Krøyer

Maestoso
f
1. Der er et yn-digt Land, det staar med bre-de Bø-ge nær
1. I know a love-ly land, Whose charm-ing woods of bee-ches Grow
sal-ten Ø-ster-strand, nær sal-ten Ø-ster-strand.
near the Bal-tic strand, Grow near the Bal-tic strand.
cresc.
f
p
Det bug-ter sig i Bak-ke, Dal, det hed-der gam-le
It waves from val-ley up to hill, Its name is ol-den
cresc.
f
p
Dan-mark, og det er Frej-as Sal, og det er Frej-as Sal.
Den-mark, And here dwells Frey-a still, And here dwells Frey-a still.
f

2. Der sad i fordums Tid
de harniskklædte Kæmper,
|: udhvilede fra Strid; :|
saa drog de frem til Fjenders Men;
nu hvile deres Bene
|: bag Højens Bavtasten. :|

3. Det Land endnu er skønt;
thi blaa sig Søen bælter,
|: og Løvet staar saa grønt; :|
og ædle Kvinder, skønne Møer
og Mænd og raske Svende
|: bebo de Danskes Øer. :|

A. Oehlenschläger

2. Here spent their quiet life
Those gallant mail-clad champions
|: Reposing from the strife. :|
From there they rushed destroying foes,
Their bones are now reposing
|: Beneath the tomb-hill's stones. :|

3. This land is charming still,
For blue are Belt and Ocean,
|: And green are woods and hill. :|
And noble women, lovely maids,
Brave men and fearless boys
|: Inhabit Denmark's isles. :|

Charles Bratli

761

Finlandia Hymn

Finlandia-hymni

Wäinö Sola

Jean Sibelius, from Op. 26, No. 7

1. O gracious Lord, by whom the morn-ing dawn-eth Now in Thy mer - cy
1. Oi, Her - ra, an - noit uu - den päi - vän koit - taa, nyt siu - naa ar - mos -
bless our na - tive land. Let Thy Light shine, to drive a - way the shad - ows,
sas i - säim - me maa! Soit aa - mu - au - rin - gon yön var - jot voit - taa
and free our homes from war's cru - el hand. To Thee our peo - ples
ja tais - ton, ah - din - gon rau - hoit - taa. Sua kan - sa kiit - tä -
pray for truth and jus - tice And in Thy faith u - ni - ted they stand.
en ain kun - ni - oit - taa ja rau - haa toi - vo - en uu - ras - taa.

2. Thy wisdom infinite is our reliance;
Thy hand shall keep our people strong and free.
They sow the seed, they humbly wait the harvest,
and give Thee thanks, whatever it be.
Our honest toil and zeal shall bring us gladness
For joy is theirs, whose hopes rest in Thee.

2. Korkeimman johtoon kansa Suomen luottaa,
vapausaarrettaan se puolustaa.
Se kylvää siemenen ja tyynnä vuottaa
satohon tyytyen, jos sen saa.
Siunaus Herran meille onnen tuottaa
ja turvan parhaimman lahjoittaa.

Translated by Marshall Kernochan

V. A. Koskenniemen sanat:

1. Oi, Suomi, katso, Sinun päiväs koittaa,
yön uhka karkoitettu on jo pois
ja aamun kiuru kirkkaudessa soittaa
kuin itse taivahan kansi sois,
yön vallat aamun valkeus jo voittaa,
sun päiväs koittaa, oi synnyinmaa.

2. Oi nouse, Suomi, nosta korkealle
pääs seppelöimä suurten muistojen,
oi nouse, Suomi, näytit maailmalle
sa että karkoitit orjuuden
ja ettet taipunut sa sorron alle,
on aamus alkanut, synnyinmaa.

God save the King

Henry Carey

Maestoso
mf
ff
1. God save our Lord, the King, Long live our no - ble King God save the King! Send him vic-
2. O Lord our God, a - rise, Scat-ter his en - e-mies, And make them fall! Con-found their
3. Thy choic-est gifts in store On him be pleas'd to pour, Long may he reign! May he de-
to - ri - ous, Hap - py and glo - ri - ous, Long to reign o - ver us; God save the King!
pol - i - tics, Frus-trate their knav-ish tricks, On Thee our hopes we fix, God save us all!
fend our laws, And ev - er give us cause To sing with heart and voice, God save the King!

La Marseillaise

Written and composed by
Claude-Joseph Rouget de Lisle (1792)

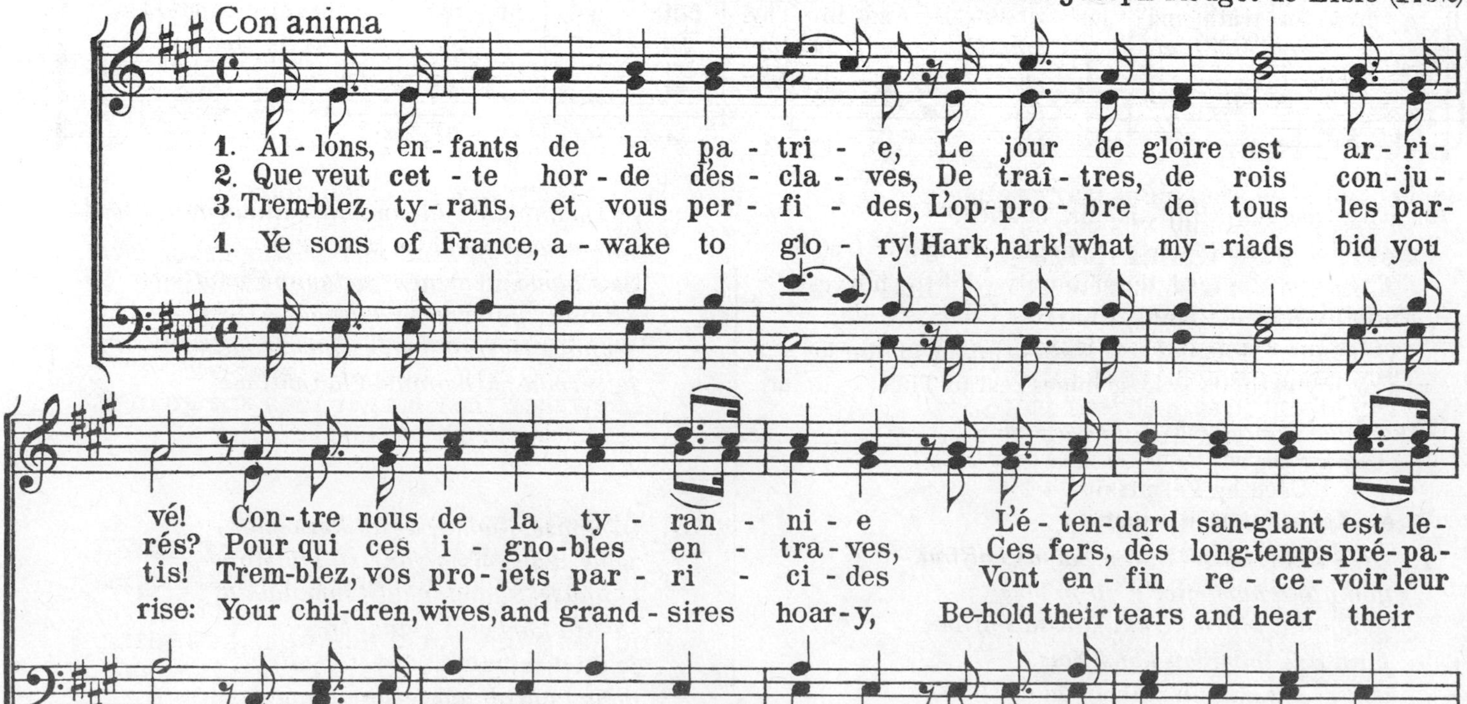

1. Al - lons, en - fants de la pa - tri - e, Le jour de gloire est ar - ri-
2. Que veut cet - te hor - de des - cla - ves, De traî - tres, de rois con - ju-
3. Trem-blez, ty - rans, et vous per - fi - des, L'op - pro - bre de tous les par-
1. Ye sons of France, a - wake to glo - ry! Hark, hark! what my - riads bid you

vé, L'é-ten-dard san-glant est le-vé! En-ten-dez-vous dans les cam-
rés? Ces fers, dès long-temps pré-pa-rés? Fran-çais! pour nous, ah! quel ou-
prix, Vont en-fin re-ce-voir leur prix. Tout est sol-dat pour vous com-
cries, Be-hold their tears and hear their cries! Shall hate-ful ty-rants, mis-chief
dim.
pa-gnes Mu-gir ces fé-ro-ces sol-dats? Ils vien-nent, jus-que dans nos
tra-ge! Quels transports il doit ex-ci-ter! C'est nous qu'on o-se me-na-
bat-tre; S'ils tom-bent, nos jeu-nes hé-ros, La France en pro-duit de nou-
breed-ing, With hire-ling hosts, a ruf-fian band, Af-fright and de-so-late the
ff
bras, É-gor-ger nos fils, nos com-pa-gnes!
cer De rendre à l'an-ti-que es-cla-va-ge.
veaux, Con-tre vous tous prêts à se bat-tre!
land, While peace and lib-er-ty lie bleed-ing?
Aux ar-mes, ci-toy-ens! For-
To arms, to arms, ye brave! Th'a-
mez vos ba-tail-lons! Mar-chez, mar-chez! qu'un sang im-pur A-breu-ve nos sil-lons!
veng-ing sword un-sheathe! March on, march on! all hearts re-solv'd On vic-to-ry or death!

4.

Français! en guerriers magnanimes,
  Portez ou retenez vos coups;
Épargnez ces tristes victimes,
  A regret s'armant contre nous;
Mais le despote sanguinaire,
  Mais les complices de Bouillé—
Tous ces tigres qui sans pitié
  Déchirent le sein de leur mère.
    Aux armes, etc.

5.

Amour sacré de la patrie,
  Conduis, soutiens nos bras vengeurs!
Liberté, Liberté chérie,
  Combats avec tes défenseurs:
Sous nos drapeaux que la victoire
  Accoure à tes mâles accents,
Que tes ennemis expirants
  Voient ton triomphe et notre gloire.
    Aux armes, etc.

2.

With luxury and pride surrounded,
  The vile, insatiate despots dare,
Their thirst of gold and power unbounded,
  To mete and vend the light and air.
Like beasts of burden would they load us,
  Like gods would bid their slaves adore;
But man is man—and who is more?
  Then shall they longer lash and goad us?
    To arms, etc.

3.

Oh liberty! can man resign thee,
  Once having felt thy generous flame?
Can dungeons, bolts and bars confine thee,
  Or whips thy noble spirit tame?
Too long the world has wept, bewailing
  That falsehood's dagger tyrants wield;
But Freedom is our sword and shield,
  And all their arts are unavailing.
    To arms, etc.

German National Anthem

Franz Joseph Haydn

Ei-nig keit und Recht und Frei-heit für das deut-sche Va-ter-land! Da-nach last uns
al-le stre-ben brü-der-lich mit Herz und Hand! Ei-nig-keit und Recht und Frei-heit
sind des Glük-kes Un-ter-pfand. Blüh im Glan-ze die-ses Glük-kes, blü-he, deutsches
Va-ter-land! Blüh im Glan-ze die-ses Glük-kes, blü-he, deutsches Va-ter-land!
8
8
8

Greece
Hymn to Freedom*
(1823)

Dionisios Solomós (1798-1857)
English version by Lorraine Noel Finley

Nicholas Manzaros
(1795-1873)

D
Maestoso
Voice
Piano
Thou art known each time the gleam - ing Of thy
Σὲ γνω - ρί - - - ζ'ἀ - πὸ τὴν κό - ψι, Τοῦ σπα -
sword ap - pears out - lined, Thou art known by pow'r re -
θιοῦ τὴν τρο - με - ρὴ Σὲ γνω - ρί - ζ'ἀ - πὸ τὴν
deem - ing And em - brac - ing all man - kind. From the
ὄ - ψι, Ποῦ μὲ βιὰ με - τράει τὴν γῆ 'Απ' τὰ

*Greece won its independence from Turkey after a desperate struggle lasting from 1821 to 1833. The words of "The Hymn to Freedom" were written in 1823 and set to music in 1828. The song was officially adopted as the Greek national anthem in 1864.

mar - tyrs per - se - cut - ed, From all Greeks where-e'er they be, Thou art
κοκ - κα - λα βγαλ-μέ - νη, Τῶν Ἑλ - λή - νων - τὰ ἱ ε - ρὰ Καὶ σὰν
brave - ly now sa - lut - ed, Hail, O Free - dom, all hail to thee! Thou art
πρῶ - τα ἀν-δρει - ω - μέ - νη, Χαῖ - ρε, ὢ χαῖ - ρε ἐ - λευ - θε - ριά! Καὶ σὰν
brave - ly now sa - lu - ted, Hail, O Free - dom! Hail to thee!
πρῶ - τα ἀνδρει-ω - μέ - νη, Χαῖ - ρε, ὢ χαῖ - ρε ἐ-λευ θε - ριά!

Italian National Anthem

Novaro

Andante Maetoso.
f
p Fra -
tel - li d'I - ta - lia, l'I - ta - lia s'e de - sta; Del -
l'el - mo di Sci - pio s'é cin - ta la tes - ta. Do -
vié, la vit - to - ria Le por - ge la chio - ma, ché
schia - va di Ro - ma Id - di - o la cre - ó.
f

p
Strin-giamci in co - or - te, strin-giamci in co - or - te, Vo - lia - mo alla
3
mor - te, ché Ita - lia chia - mo',— Strin-giamci in co - or - te, strin giamci in co -
f
or - te, vo lia - mo alla mor - te, ché Ita - lia chia - mo'. Strin-giamci in co -
or - te, vo - lia - mo alla mor - te, vo - lia - mo alla mor - te, ché Ita - lia chia -
cresc.
mo'. Strin-giamci in co - or - te, strin-giam-ci in co - or te, vo - lia - mo alla
ff
1.2 ecc.
Last
mor - te, ché Ita - lia chia - mo'. Ché Ita - lia, ché Ita - lia, chia - mo'.

Mexico

Himno Nacional*

(1854)

Francisco González Bocanegra
(1824-1861)
English version by Lorraine Noel Finley

Jaime D. Nuñó
(1825-1903)

Chorus
Alla marcia
Voice
Piano
Fel - low coun - try - men, Mex - i - co needs you; Have your
Mé - xi - ca - nos, al gri - to de gue - rra El a -
bay - o - nets read - y to wield, Then ride forth where your fa - ther - land
ce - ro a - pres - tad y el bri - dón, Y re - tiem - ble en sus cen - tros la
leads you To the roar - ing of guns on the field, Then ride
tie - rra, Al so - no - ro ru - gir del ca - ñón. Y re -

*The words were chosen from a competition held by the Government between 25 poets of note. Señor Nuñó was conductor of the National Military Band when he composed the music. In later life he removed to Buffalo, N. Y. where he resided until his death in 1903. In Oct. 1942 his body was disinterred, flown to Mexico City in a bomber and buried there with impressive patriotic ceremonies.

Fine
forth where your fa-ther-land leads — you To the roar-ing of guns on—the field.
tiem-ble en sus cen-tros la tie - rra Al so-no-ro ru-gir del—ca-ñón.
ff
Solo
p
O my coun-try, your sons— swear de-vo - - tion, To de-
¡Pa-tria! ¡pa-tria! tus hi - jos te ju - - ran Ex-ha-
p
fend — you is their— true en-deav - - or; If the
lar— en tus a - ras su a-lien - - to Si el cla-
trum-pet has called, they will ev - er Fight the bat - tle with cour-age held
rín con su bé - li-co a-cen - to Los con-vo - ca a li-diar con va-

p
high. Now for you are the gar-lands of va-lor, And the
lor. ¡Pa-ra tí las guir-nal-das de o-li-va! ¡Un re-
f
p
mem-'ry of them,— for your glo-ry! Vic-t'ry's
cuer-do pa-ra e-llos de glo-ria! ¡Un lau-
lau-rel has told all the sto-ry: Hon-or's grave a-waits all those who may
rel pa-ra tí de vic-to-ria! ¡Un se-pul-cro pa-ra e-llos de ho-
D.C. al Fine
die! Hon-or's grave a-waits all those who may die!
nor! ¡Un— se-pul-cro pa-ra e-llos de ho-nor!
ff

The Netherlands

Wilhelmus van Nassouwe

(1568)

Dutch text anonymous*
English version by Lorraine Noel Finley

"The Tune of Charters"
(French Huguenot melody of the 17th century)

Maestoso
Voice
Piano
I, *Wil - liam, Count of *Nas - sau, Of an - cient
Wil - hel - mus van Nas - sou - we Ben ik van
Dutch de - scent, To Fa - ther - land am
Diet - schen bloed, Den Va - der - land ge -
loy - al Un - til my life is spent! A
trou - we Blijf ik tot in den dood; Een

*William the Silent (1533-1584), Count of Nassau and Prince of Orange, was *"Stadholder"* or Protector of the Netherlands under the overlordship of Philip II, King of Spain. In this ballad, William denies that he violated his oath of allegiance to Philip, although he resisted by force of arms the tyrannical infringements of the civil and religious liberties of the Dutch people

Prince of *Or - ange I am Yet un -
Prin - - - ce van O - ran - jen Ben ik
daunt - ed and free; The King___ of
vrij on - ver - veerd Den Ko - - - ning
Spain has known me Ev - er faith - ful___ to be.
van His - pan - jen Heb ik al - tijd___ ge - ëerd.

***perpetrated by Spanish officials. The song has 15 verses, the first letters of which make an acrostic of "William of Nassau" Many historians have attributed the words to Marnix van St. Aldegone, a general in William's army.**

Norway

Ja, vi elsker

(1859)

Björnstjerne Björnson*
(1832-1910)

Richard Nordraak*
(1842-1866)

Maestoso
Voice
Piano
f
Yes, we love this land, our coun - try, With her thou - sand
Ja, vi els - ker det - te lan - det, Som det sti - ger
homes, Lift - ing high her storm - lashed moun - tains
frem Fu - ret vær - bitt o - ver van - net
Where the North Sea foams.
Med de tu - sen hjem;—
p
Yes, we love her, and re -
El - sker, el sker det, og

*Björnson is well-known to the English speaking world as one of Norway's great dramatists and poets. The poem "Ja, vi elsker" swept the country by storm and in 1862, Nordraak, the great friend of Grieg, set it to music and it was soon adopted as the national anthem.

mem - ber those who gave us birth, And the
ten - ker Paa vaar far og mor Og den
an - cient sa - gas bring - ing Dreams up - on our earth. And the
sa - ga - natt, som sen - ker Dröm - me paa vaar jord, Og den
an - cient sa - gas bring - ing, bring - ing Dreams up - on our earth.
sa - ga - natt, som sen - ker sen - ker Dröm - me paa vor jord.
f
f

The Commonwealth of the Philippines

(1898)*

José Palma

Julian Felipe

Alla marcia
Voice
Piano
Land of the morn - ing, Child of the sun re-turn - ing,
Land dear and ho - ly, Cra - dle of no - ble he - roes,
1.
2.
With fer-vor burn - ing, Thee do our souls a - dore.
Ne'er shall in - vad - ers
Tram-ple thy sa - cred shore.
Ev - er with - in thy skies and thro' thy clouds And o'er thy hills and sea, Do we be -
Thy ban - ner, dear to all our hearts, Its sun and stars a - light, O

*The National Anthem was written at the suggestion of General Aguinaldo, leader of the Filipino revolt against Spanish rule in 1896 to 1898.

hold the ra - diance, feel the throb, Of glo - rious lib - er - ty.
nev - er shall its shin - ing field Be dimmed by ty - rant's might.
Con spirito
ff
Beau - ti - ful land of love, O land of light, In thine em -
brace 'tis rap - ture to lie; But it is glo - ry ev - er, when
thou art wronged, For us, thy sons, to suf - fer and die.

Swedish National Anthem

Svensk folkmelodi
Arr.: Josef Jonsson (1946)

Moderato
mf
Du gam - la, du fri - a, du fjäll - hö - ga Nord, du
Du tro - nar på min - nen från forn - sto - ra dar, då
Thou an - cient, thou free - born, Thou moun - tain - ous North, In
Thy throne rests on mem'-ries From great days of yore, When
E
tys - ta, du gläd - je - ri - ka skö - na! Jag häl - sar dig, vä - nas - te land up - på jord, din
ä - rat ditt namn flög ö - ver jor - den. Jag vet, att du är och du blir, vad du var, ja,
beau - ty and peace our hearts be - guil - ing, I greet thee, thou love - li - est land on the earth, Thy
world - wide re - nown was val - our's guerdon. I know to thy name thou art true as be - fore. Oh,
non rit.
f
sol, din himmel, di - na äng - der grö - na, din sol, din himmel, di - na ängder grö - na.
jag vill le - va, jag vill dö i Nor - den, ja, jag vill le - va, jag vill dö i Nor - den.
sun, thy skies, thy verdant meadows smil - ing, thy sun, thy skies, thy verdant meadows smil - ing.
I would live and I would die in Swe - den, Oh, I would live and I would die in Swe - den.
Translation by Noel Wirén

America

Samuel Francis Smith | Henry Carey

1. My coun - try, 'tis of thee, Sweet land of lib - er - ty, Of thee I
2. My na - tive coun - try, thee, Land of the no - ble free, Thy name I
sing. Land where my fa - thers died; Land of the pil - grim's pride; From ev - 'ry
love. I love thy rocks and rills, Thy woods and tem - pled hills; My heart with
moun - tain - side Let free - dom ring.
rap - ture thrills, Like that a - bove.
3. Let mu - sic swell the breeze, And ring from
4. Our fa - thers' God! to Thee, Au - thor of
all the trees Sweet free - dom's song; Let mor - tal tongues a - wake, Let all that
lib - er - ty, To Thee we sing; Long may our land be bright With free - dom's
breathe par - take, Let rocks their si - lence break, The sound pro - long.
ho - ly light; Pro - tect us by Thy might, Great God, our King.

America, The Beautiful

Katherine Lee Bates

Samuel A. Ward

Moderato
Voice
Piano
mf
1. O beau-ti-ful for spa-cious skies, For am-ber waves of grain, For
3. O beau-ti-ful for he-roes proved In lib-er-at-ing strife, Who
pur-ple moun-tain maj-es-ties A-bove the fruit-ed plain. A-
more than self their coun-try loved, And mer-cy more than life. A-
f
mer-i-ca! A-mer-i-ca! God shed His grace on thee, And
mer-i-ca! A-mer-i-ca! May God thy gold re-fine Till
crown thy good with broth-er-hood From sea to shin-ing sea.
all suc-cess be no-ble-ness And ev-'ry gain, di-vine.

Published, MCMXLII, by Boston Music Co.

mf
2. O beau - ti - ful for pil - grim feet Whose stern im - pas - sioned stress A
4. O beau - ti - ful for pa - triot dream That sees be - yond the years Thine
mf
thor - ough - fare for free - dom beat A - cross the wil - der - ness. A -
al - a - bas - ter cit - ies gleam Un - dimm'd by hu - man tears. A -
f
f
mer - i - ca! A - mer - i - ca! God mend thine ev - 'ry flaw, Con -
mer - i - ca! A - mer - i - ca! God shed His grace on thee, And
D. C.
firm thy soul in self - con - trol, Thy lib - er - ty in law.
crown thy good with broth - er - hood From sea to shin - ing sea.
D. C.

Battle-Hymn of the Republic

Julia Ward Howe

1. Mine___ eyes have seen the glo - ry of the
2. I have seen Him in the watch - fires of a
3. I have read a fier - y gos - pel writ in
4. He has sound - ed forth the trum - pet that shall
5. In the beau - ty of the lil - ies Christ was
com - ing of the Lord; He is tramp - ling out the vin - tage where the
hun - dred cir - cling camps; They have build - ed Him an al - tar in the
bur - nished rows of steel: "As ye deal with my con - tem - ners, so with
nev - er call re - treat; He is sift - ing out the hearts of men be -
born a - cross the sea, With a glo - ry in His bo - som that trans -
grapes of wrath are stored; He hath loosed the fate - ful light - ning of His
eve - ning dews and damps; I can read His right - eous sen - tence by the
you my grace shall deal." Let the He - ro born of wo - man crush the
fore His judg - ment - seat: Oh, be swift, my soul, to an - swer Him! be
fig - ures you and me: As He died to make men ho - ly, let us
ter - ri - ble swift sword; His truth___ is march - ing on.
dim and flar - ing lamps: His day___ is march - ing on.
ser - pent with his heel, Since God___ is march - ing on.
ju - bi - lant, my feet! Our God___ is march - ing on.
die to make men free, While God___ is march - ing on.

CHORUS

S. & A.
Glo - ry! glo - ry! Hal - le - lu - jah! Glo - ry! glo - ry! Hal - le - lu - jah!
T. & B.
Glo - ry! glo - ry! Hal - le - lu - jah! His truth is march - ing on.

Dixie Land

Dan Emmet

Allegro

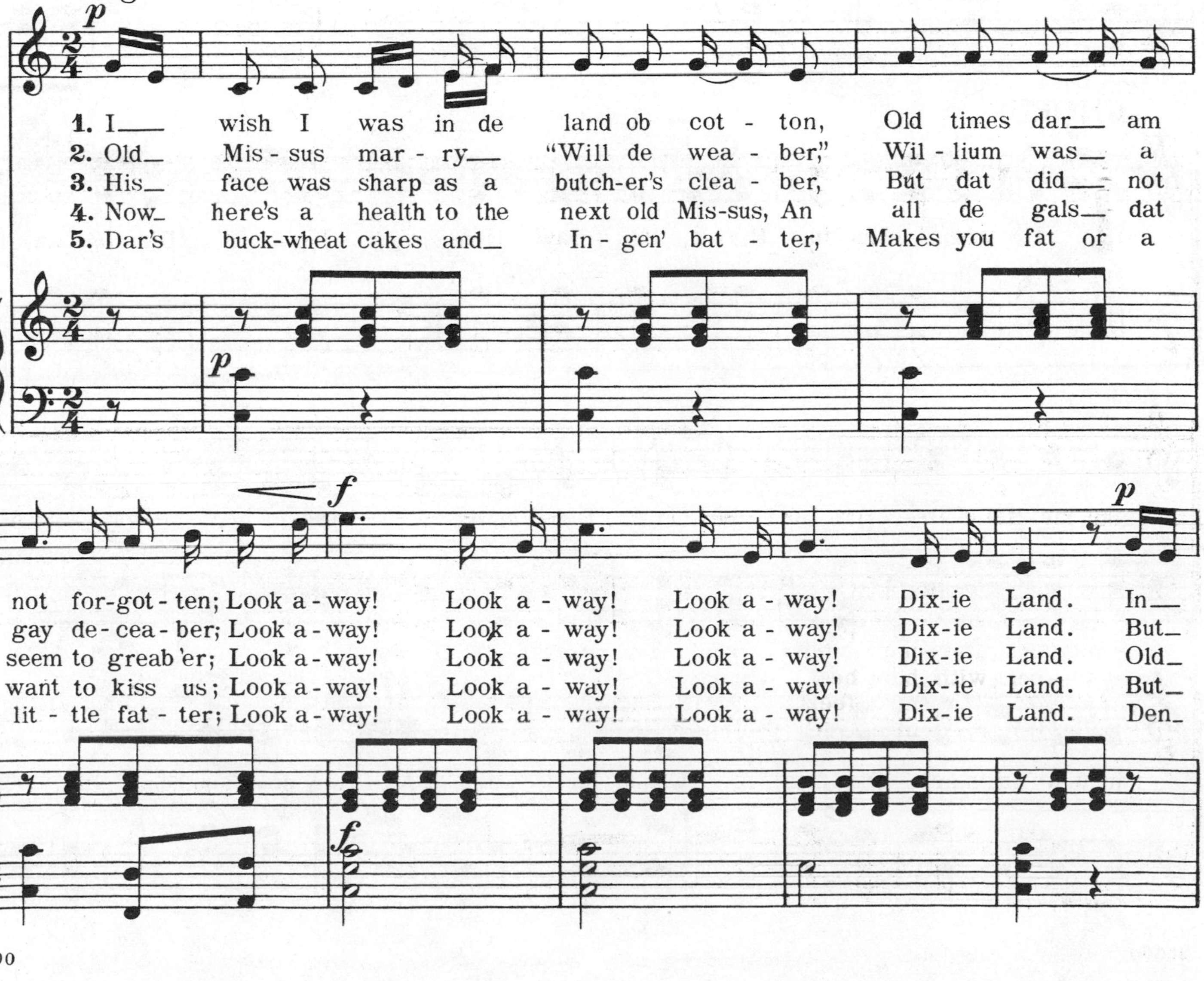

Dix - ie Land whar I was born in, Ear - ly on one frost - y morn - in',
when he put his arm a - round 'er, He smiled as fierce as a for - ty - pound - er,
Mis - sus act - ed de fool - ish part And died for a man dat broke her heart,
if you want to drive 'way sor - row Come and hear dis song to - mor - row,
hoe it down an scratch your grab - ble, To Dix - ie's land I'm bound to trab - ble,
Look a - way! Look a - way! Look a - way! Dix - ie Land.
p
f
CHORUS
Den I wish I was in Dix - ie, Hoo - ray! Hoo - ray! In Dix - ie Land I'll take my stand To lib and die in Dix - ie, A - way, A - way, A - way down south in Dix - ie, A - way, A - way, A - way down south in Dix - ie.

Dedicated to the U. S. Field Artillery

The Caissons Go Rolling Along

By Brig Gen. Edmund L. Gruber

March time
Piano
Voice
O-ver hill, o-ver dale, We have hit the dust-y trail, And those
To the front, day and night, Where the dough-boys dig and fight, And those
cais-sons go roll-ing a-long;
cais-sons go roll-ing a-long;
"Coun-ter march! Right a-bout!" Hear those
Our bar-rage will be there Fi-red
wa-gon sol-diers shout, While those cais-sons go roll-ing a-long:
on the rock-et's flare While those cais-sons go roll-ing a-long:

Chorus
For it's Hi! Hi! Hee! in the Field Ar-til-le-ry, Call off your
num-bers loud and strong, And where-e'er we go You will al-ways know That those
(Call off)
cais-sons go roll-ing a-long, That those cais-sons go roll-ing a-
(Keep 'em roll-ing)
1.
long, For it's
2.
long,
After Last Chorus
rit.
Bat-t'ry Hal-------t
ff rit.

Hail, Columbia!

Joseph Hopkinson

Phyla

1. Hail, Co-lum - bia, hap - py land! Hail, ye he - roes! heav'n-born band! Who
2. Im - mor - tal pa - triots! rise once more, De - fend your rights; de - fend your shore; Let
3. Sound, sound the trump of fame! Let Wash - ing - ton's great name Ring
4. Be - hold, the Chief who now com - mands, Once more to serve his coun - try stands, The
fought and bled in Free - dom's cause, Who fought and bled in Free - dom's cause, And
no rude foe with im - pious hand, Let no rude foe with im - pious hand In -
through the world with loud ap - plause, Ring through the world with loud ap - plause, Let
rock on which the storm will beat; The rock on which the storm will beat; But
when the storm of war was gone, En - joyed the peace your val - or won. Let
vade the shrine, where sa - cred lies, Of toil and blood the well-earned prize. While
ev - 'ry clime to free - dom dear Lis - ten with a joy - ful ear. With
armed in vir - tue, firm and true His hopes are fixed on heav'n and you. When
in - de - pen - dence be our boast, Ev - er mind - ful what it cost;
of - f'ring peace, sin - cere and just, In heav'n we place a man - ly trust, That
e - qual skill, with god - like pow'r, He gov - erns in the fear - ful hour Of
hope was sink - ing in dis - may, When gloom ob - scured Co - lum - bia's day, His
Ev - er grate - ful for the prize, Let its al - tar reach the skies.
Truth and Jus - tice will pre - vail, And ev - 'ry scheme of bond - age fail.
hor - rid war, or guides with ease The hap - pier times of hon - est peace.
stead - y mind, from chan - ges free, Re - solved on death or lib - er - ty.

Firm, u - nit - ed, let__ us__ be, Rally - ing round our lib - er - ty;
As a band of__ broth - ers__ joined, Peace__ and__ safe - ty we shall find.

Marching through Georgia

Words and Music by
Henry C. Work

Tempo di marcia
f
fz
Fine
1. Bring the good old bu - gle, boys, we'll sing an - oth - er song,
2. How the dar - kies shout - ed when they heard the joy - ful sound;
3. Yes, and there were U - nion men who wept with joy - ful tears,
4. "Sher - man's dash - ing Yank - ee boys will nev - er reach the coast!"
5. So we made a thor - ough - fare for Free - dom and her train,
mf march time
Sing it with a spir - it that will start the world a - long, Sing it as we used to sing it,
How the tur - keys gob - bled which our com - mis - sa - ry found; How the sweet po - ta - toes e - ven
When they saw the honoured flag they had not seen for years; Hard - ly could they be restrain'd from
So the sau - cy reb - els said, and 'twas a handsome boast; Had they not for - got, a - las, to
Six - ty miles in lat - i - tude, three hun - dred to the main; Trea - son fled be - fore us, for re -
cresc.

f
fif - ty thou - sand strong,
start - ed from the ground,
breark - ing forth in cheers,
reck - on with the host,
sist - ance was in vain,
While we were march - ing through Geor - gia.
CHORUS
Hur - rah, hur - rah, we bring the Ju - bi - lee! Hur -
Hur - rah, hur - rah, we bring the Ju - bi - lee!
rah, hur - rah, the flag that makes you free! So we sang the cho - rus from At -
Hur - rah, hur - rah, the flag that makes you free! So we sang the cho - rus from At -
lan - ta to the sea, While we were march - ing through Geor - gia.
lan - ta to the sea, While we were march - ing through Geor - gia.

The Marines' Hymn

Arranged by
Jeffrey Marlowe

Official Song of the
United States Marine Corps

Quick March time
Piano
f
Voice
1. From the halls of Mon-te-zu - ma To the shores of Trip-o - li; We fight our coun-try's bat - tles In the
2. Our flag's un-furl'd to ev - 'ry breeze From dawn to set-ting sun, We have fought in ev-'ry clime and place Where
3. Here's health to you and to our Corps Which we are proud to serve; In man-y a strife we've fought for life, And

Used by permission of the United States Marine Corps.

air, on land, and sea. First to fight for right and free - dom And to
we could take a gun; In the snow of far - off north-ern lands And in
nev - er lost our nerve. If the Ar - my and the Na - vy Ev - er
keep our hon-or clean, We are proud to claim the ti - tle Of U-
sun-ny trop-ic scenes, You will find us al - ways on the job, The U-
look on heav-en's scenes, They will find the streets are guard - ed By U-
1st and 2nd verse
3rd verse
nit - ed States Ma - rine.
nit - ed States Ma - rines.
nit - ed States Ma - rines.
sf
sf

Columbia, The Gem of the Ocean

The Red, White, and Blue

David T. Shaw

Thomas A. Becket

Oh, Co - lum - bia, the gem of the o - cean, The
When war wing'd its wide des - o - la - tion, And
The star - span - gled ban - ner bring hith - er, O'er Co-
home of the brave and the free, The shrine of each pa-triot's de -
threat - end the land to de - form, The ark then of free - dom's foun -
lum - bia's true sons let it wave; May the wreaths they have won nev - er
vo - tion, A world of - fers hom - age to thee; Thy
da - tion, Co - lum - bia, rode safe thro' the storm; With the
with - er, Nor its stars cease to shine on the brave; May the
man - dates make he - roes as - sem - ble, When Lib - er - ty's form stands in
gar - lands of vic - t'ry a - round her, When so proud - ly she bore her brave
ser - vice u - nit - ed ne'er sev - er, But hold to their col - ors so
view; Thy ban - ners make tyr - an - ny trem - ble, When
crew, With her flag proud - ly float - ing be - fore her, The
true; The Ar - my and Na - vy for ev - er! Three

borne by the red, white, and blue! When borne by the red, white, and
boast of the red, white, and blue! The boast of the red, white, and
cheers for the red, white, and blue! Three cheers for the red, white, and
blue! When borne by the red, white, and blue! Thy
blue! The boast of the red, white, and blue! With her
blue! Three cheers for the red, white, and blue! The
ban-ners make tyr-an-ny trem-ble, When borne by the red, white, and blue!
flag proud-ly float-ing be-fore her, The boast of the red, white, and blue!
Ar-my and Na-vy for ev-er! Three cheers for the red, white, and blue!

The Star-Spangled Banner

Francis Scott (1814) J. Stafford Smith

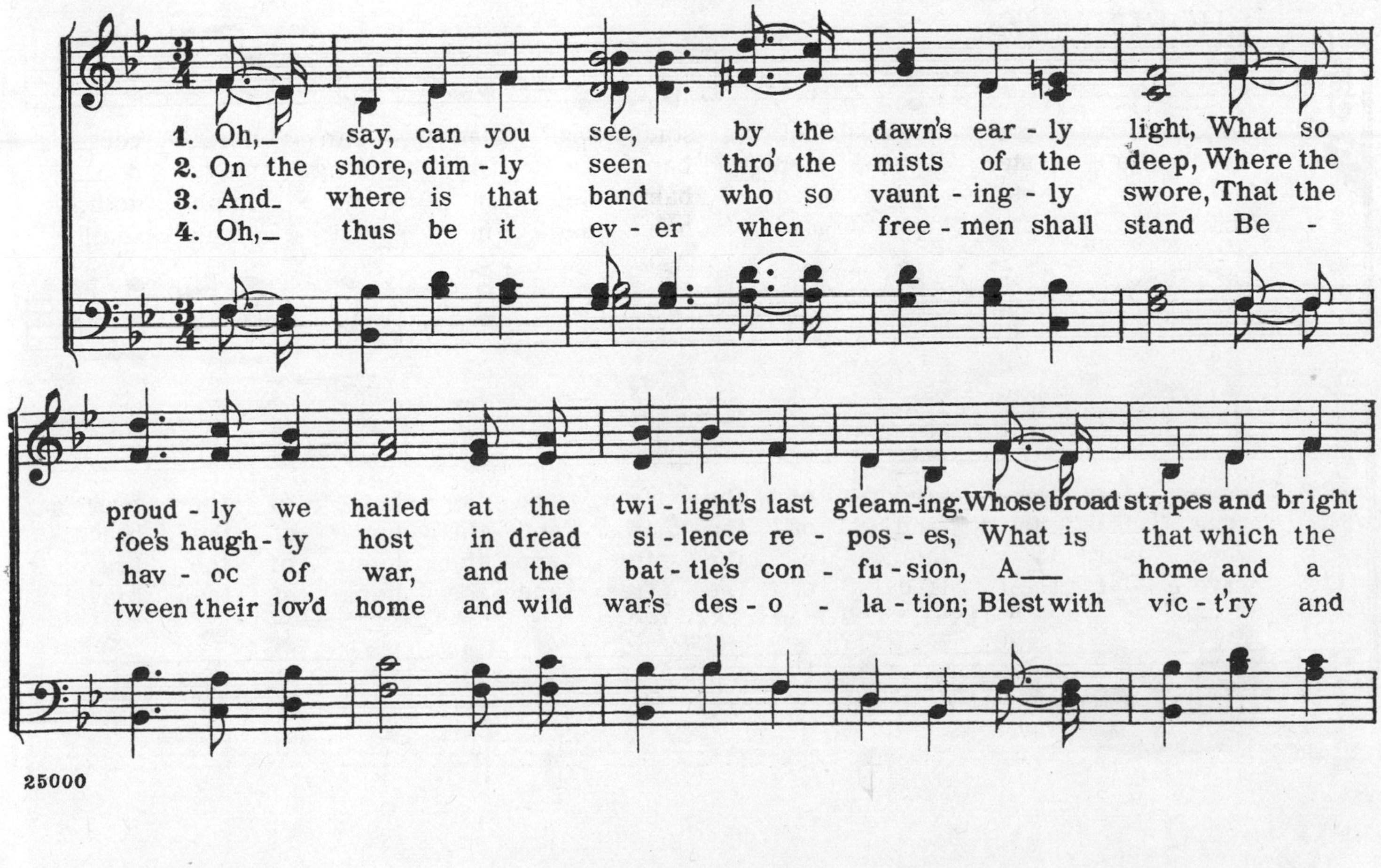
1. Oh, say, can you see, by the dawn's ear-ly light, What so
2. On the shore, dim-ly seen thro' the mists of the deep, Where the
3. And where is that band who so vaunt-ing-ly swore, That the
4. Oh, thus be it ev-er when free-men shall stand Be-
proud-ly we hailed at the twi-light's last gleam-ing, Whose broad stripes and bright
foe's haugh-ty host in dread si-lence re-pos-es, What is that which the
hav-oc of war, and the bat-tle's con-fu-sion, A home and a
tween their lov'd home and wild war's des-o-la-tion; Blest with vic-t'ry and

stars, thro' the per - il - ous flight, O'er the ram-parts we watch'd were so
breeze, o'er the tow - er - ing steep, As it fit - ful - ly blows, half con -
coun - try should leave us no more? Their_ blood has wash'd out their foul
peace, may the heav'n-res-cued land Praise the Pow'r that hath made and pre -
gal - lant - ly stream-ing? And the rock - ets' red glare, the bombs
ceals, half dis - clos - es? Now it catch - es the gleam of the
foot - steps' pol - lu - tion! No___ ref - uge could save___ the
serv'd us a na - tion. Then_ con - quer we must, when our
burst-ing in air, Gave proof thro' the night that our flag was still there.
morn-ing's first beam, In full glo - ry re - flect - ed, now shines on the stream:
hire-ling and slave From the ter - ror of flight or the gloom of the grave:
cause it is just, And_ this be our mot - to: "In___ God is our trust!"
CHORUS
ff
Oh,___ say does that star - span - gled ban - ner_ yet_
'Tis the star - span - gled ban - ner! Oh, long may_ it___
And the star - span - gled ban - ner in tri - umph doth_
And the star - span - gled ban - ner in tri - umph shall_
cresc.
ff
wave O'er the land_ of the free, and the home of the brave?
wave O'er the land of the free, and the home of the brave!
wave O'er the land_ of the free, and the home of the brave!
wave O'er the land of the free, and the home of the brave!

Yankee Doodle

Dr. Schackburg

1. Fath'r and I went down to camp, A - long with Cap - tain
2. And there we see a thou - sand men, As rich as Squire
3. And there was Cap - tain Wash - ing - ton Up - on a slap - ping
4. And then the feath - ers on his hat, They looked so ver - y
Good - 'in, And there we saw the men and boys As thick as has - ty pud - din'.
Da - vid; And what they wast - ed ev - 'ry day, I wish it could be sav - ed.
stal - lion, A giv - ing or - ders to his men; I guess there was a mil - lion.
fine, ah! I want - ed pes - ki - ly to get, To give to my Je - mi - ma.
CHORUS
Yan - kee Doo - dle, keep it up, Yan - kee Doo - dle dan - dy,
Mind the mu - sic and the step, And with the girls be han - dy.

5 And there I see a swamping gun,
Large as a log of maple,
Upon a mighty little cart;
A load for father's cattle.

6 And every time they fired it off,
It took a horn of powder;
It made a noise like father's gun,
Only a nation louder.

7 And there I see a little keg,
Its head all made of leather,
They knocked upon't with little sticks
To call the folks together.

8 And Cap'n Davis had a gun,
He kind o' clapt his hand on't
And stuck a crooked stabbing-iron
Upon the little end on't.

9 The troopers, too, would gallop up
And fire right in our faces;
It scared me almost half to death
To see them run such races.

10 It scared me so I hooked if off,
Nor stopped, as I remember,
Nor turned about till I got home,
Locked up in mother's chamber

INDEX ACCORDING TO TITLES

PIANO

25000

PIANO (*Continued*)

ORGAN

VOCAL

25000

VOCAL (*Continued*)

25000

INDEX ACCORDING TO COMPOSERS

PIANO

25000

ORGAN

VOCAL

25000